MR BOWLER OF BATH

Jonathan Burdett Bowler, 1834-1911 (BIHC Archive)

Mr Bowler of Bath

Victorian Entrepreneur and Engineer

Ken Andrews

Published in 1998 by
Ken Andrews
35 Kellaway Avenue
Westbury Park
Bristol   BS6 7XS

Layout and typesetting by
EX LIBRIS PRESS
1 The Shambles
Bradford on Avon
Wiltshire

Printed in Britain by
Cromwell Press
Trowbridge
Wiltshire

ISBN 0 9534201 0 8

To Valerie

Contents

Acknowledgements

My acknowledgements and thanks are due to:
Stuart Burroughs, the Curator of the Bath Industrial Heritage Centre,
for his willing help and permission to research the Bowler Archive.;
Gerald Christie for his cooperation and assistance in the reshelving,
identifying and labelling of the Bowler Books; Don Browning for
permission to use his drawings of the treadle lathe and shaping
machine, and photographs of the artefacts in the collection; Mrs Joan
Day for the photograph of the brass cranes; Mr Frank Ludlow for
his help on the Madame Alyce research; Professor R. Angus
Buchanan for his comments on the evolution of the professional
engineer; Gerald Hart for pointing me to the 'Inglis' reference in the
introduction; Colin Johnstone and staff at the Guildhall Archive, Bath;
the staff at the Bath Reference Library; my Tutor, Dr Graham Davis,
for his very helpful tutorials at which the progress of the Dissertation,
from which this book was written, was discussed; finally, my wife,
Valerie, for her patient help with proof reading and forbearance when
my mind has been with Mr Bowler and his works.

Introduction

Jonathan Burdett Bowler began an apprenticeship in 1848, at the age of fourteen. He showed considerable flair and acumen and grew to become a prominent Bath businessman and entrepreneur. He built a business that became known nationwide and even internationally among people requiring mineral water manufacturing machinery. Alongside the manufacture of this machinery he also acquired a reputation for doing practically anything asked of him – if he couldn't do it, which was rare, he would find someone who could. In the course of his mineral water machinery repair activities he acquired a mineral water manufactory, possibly by default of payment of the bills he submitted to the original owner, thus enhancing his business activities even further.

The business very soon became well known by engineers, builders and the general public as a source of supply for a multiplicity of materials from bell hanging equipment to spare keys, nuts and bolts, metal cut or machined to any shape or size, plumbing and gas fittings. He was also well known for repairs. Many items in the early days were not made on a mass production scale and no 'off the shelf' spare parts were available, so Bowler and his men would repair the item or make a new one quite often actioned by a peremptory demand such as 'have ready by this afternoon, manservant will collect'. Perhaps surprisingly, as there is no obvious connection, he also did painting and decorating though, as previously stated, he would do practically anything asked of him – there is even a record of him laying a garden path. He attended auctions and bought anything that could be sold on, used as scrap for melting down in his foundry or repaired and then sold on to his customers.

Excess profits made from his business were used to purchase

property which he sold as required to fund further business expansion and, when profits accumulated, again he bought more property.

He died in 1911 having suffered a stroke in his later years, and soon after his death twelve of his thirteen children formed a limited liability company that took the business to its closure in 1969. When the business closed Russell Frears, a local businessman, after protracted negotiation with Ernest Bowler, the final manager of the business, purchased the contents for £2,000, and with others formed The Bath Industrial Heritage Trust (BIHT) to preserve the contents of the Corn Street premises, now known as 'The Bowler Collection'.[1] Russell Frear's interest in the business had been stimulated by a visit to the shop to purchase some metal. Looking around the shop it became obvious that many of the contents were extremely old. Eventually he managed to persuade Ernest Bowler to give him a conducted tour around the premises, and what he saw then led to the birth of the Bowler Collection.

The building and its contents were photographed to provide a record so that the items could be set up in the future as a museum exhibition to resemble as closely as possible the original layout of the business. This had to be done fairly quickly as the building was subject to a compulsory purchase order, the site being required for the new Avon Street multi-storey Car Park. A problem then arose because there was no suitable site to house this very large and unique collection, so a temporary storage site was found in Walcot Street until a suitable permanent one became available. Eventually, in 1978, the collection was moved into the Camden Works, now also known as the Bath Industrial Heritage Centre (BIHC), in Julian Road. This was built in 1777 as a Real or Royal Tennis Court (a 12th Century, French racquet and ball game) and had become, amongst other things, a pin manufactory.[2] Using the photographs of the original set up the Collection has been arranged to give, as far as possible, the feel of the original premises, complete with sound effects.

During the life of the business most of the machinery that had been bought by Bowler and his successors, practically all at second hand, remained unchanged and matériel which was surplus or thought to have a possible future use was retained, together with much of the documentation from the early days to closure – the Archive contains more than 80,000 invoices, letters, receipts, orders and books of the business spanning the period 1834-1969.[3] Unfortunately, not all of the books or documents survived and this makes a complete picture of the business impossible to obtain, especially in the final years.

When this study began the documents had been sorted, catalogued, card indexed and boxed, but the books had not. This made it difficult to assess the information available so it was decided to make a database as a means of cataloguing the books. During the preparation of the database new shelves were provided for the books by a BIHC volunteer (Mr G. A. Christie) and as a joint effort with the author and Mr Christie they were labelled, wrapped, boxed and shelved. Rapid access to any of the books is now possible by reference to the database reports or the box labels.

There is no doubt that the most interesting period of the business is that during Jonathan Bowler's lifetime and it is that period for which, fortunately, most of the documents survive. To a certain extent the business seemed to rest on its laurels from the time of Bowler's death relying on reputation rather than innovation, though as suppliers they certainly kept up with the times and even ventured into the emergent motor trade for a while, having opened the Ambury Motor Works.

Eventually with the death of Bowler's children, his grandson, Ernest Bowler, took over and allowed the business to coast into decline having no one else in the family willing to take it on. This was helped, perhaps, by other suppliers' improved sales techniques and the advent of the 'Do It Yourself' supermarket. The actual closure of the business was precipitated by the execution of the compulsory purchase order for the construction of the Avon Street multi-storey car park.

Many books have been written on the City of Bath, mostly covering its upper classes and architecture; until recent years most authors seemed to consider that there was no industry or lower social class life in Bath. Indeed, Inglis in 1960 stated that 'Colchester, Exeter and Bath had not been touched by industry in 1851'.[4] But by that time Bath industries had become quite extensive. Bath was becoming well known for its cabinet and carriage making; the cloth industries of Twerton and Weston were growing, though these two outlying areas were not yet part of Bath.

The chapter on Bowler's associated trades in Bath demonstrates that there was also a significant and growing metal trades industry in Bath at that period and, using the Bath Street Directories, plots the growth of the trades from 1783-1866. Many of these businesses may have been run as back of shop activities, but nevertheless contributed as a whole to Bath's growing industries.

Tables 5 and 6 provide firm evidence that the extent of the metal trades in Bath was on a greater scale than hitherto recognised. This is further evidence of small-scale industry in Bath as noted by R.S. Neale and others, so qualifying our understanding of this period of Bath's history. The study of Bowler's business offers an example of the eclectic range of activities in one firm, its rapid response to new demands and how like many other Bath businesses it operated, not only locally but on a national and even international scale.

The Early Years
1834-1872

J onathan Burdett Bowler kept a book which has become known, in the Bowler Archive, as 'Bowler's Book'.[1] The Archive is located at the Bath Industrial Heritage Centre. The Book begins 'This book belongs to Jonathan Burdett Bowler born 7 January, 1834 at Bath, Somersetshire. Written by J. Bowler, Scholar, 1852'. It is neither wholly a journal nor even a narrative in the full sense, but a miscellany, which gives a wealth of information about his early days including his employment and family history, providing a story of life and social history at that time. There are recipes to make paint, another for 'brilliant white stone whitewash, which will retain its brilliance for many years', there is also a table giving the weights of different ingredients required to make alloys, e.g. guilding metals, metal for house bells and for gunmetal cocks etc. For example, to make gunmetal the ingredients are: 16 lbs. of copper, 4 lbs. of brass, 1 lb. of tin and 4 oz. of lead.

The Book demonstrates his ability, industry and determination to succeed in spite of life's vagaries – his father died at an early age leaving him as nominal head of his family at the age of twenty years, whilst still an apprentice, with an ailing mother and a four year old brother to care for.

Bowler was the fourth child of Frederick Edward Bowler and Mary Ann Woodman Bowler. He was one of eight children – three brothers, the eldest of whom (Edward) was accidentally drowned in 1841, at the age of eleven; and four sisters, two of whom (Caroline and Sarah Susannah) died in early infancy.[2] His father is first listed in the Bath Directory for 1837 as a Blacking and Ink Maker living at 12 Monmouth Place. By 1846 Bowlers parents are listed in the Bath Directory as living at The Kings Head in Walcot Street and in 1848 as landlord of the Kings Arms in Walcot Street. In this same year, on the 7 January, the young Jonathan Bowler, then fourteen years of age, commenced an Engineering Apprenticeship 'to be trained in the art of Furnishing Ironmonger and Brass Founder' with N.G. Wilcocks at the City Brass Foundry and Iron Works, where aerated water machinery was also manufactured.

At the time of the 1851 Census the family was still living in Walcot Street with Bowler's father, then aged forty-four, entered as a publican. He seemed to be prospering in the licensed trade and perhaps setting an example in the work ethic to Jonathan, because the Rate Book for that year shows him paying rates on a property at Villa Fields, Bathwick, described as a 'cottage and garden' and owned by Lord Powlett.[3]

During his apprenticeship Bowler became engaged to marry Emma Penton Blake and the wedding was arranged to take place on the 17 September 1854 at Walcot Church. This was five months before the completion of his appenticeship which had a clause stating that he could not marry during this period. Wilcocks must have looked favourably on Jonathan and waived this

Emma Penton Bowler (Photo BIHC)

clause. Sadly, one month before this, on 17 August, his father died. .
At that time his father was landlord of The Bell Tavern in River Street
Place. Providentially, his father had left them with the Bathwick
Cottage as a home, but maybe with a premonition of his own
mortality. Why Jonathan's father had rented the cottage is not clear;
was it perhaps being used as an overflow family residence? There
seems to have been no pressure to vacate the Rivers Street property
as Jonathan's wedding certificate shows his address as 2 Rivers Street.
Jonathan's astuteness, at the age of twenty, is perhaps demonstrated
by the fact that he felt able to take over the running of the family and
started almost immediately to produce a set of simple household
accounts, with some money seeming to come from his older sisters
and aunts and uncles from time to time.[4] Maybe he had seen the
operation of the account books at Wilcocks or those of his fathers'
business.

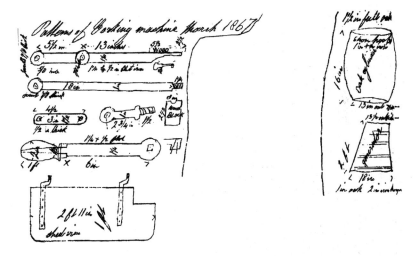

Fig 2 Drawings from Bowler's Book (computer enhanced)

Having taken on these responsibilities he started work on a
freelance basis 'moonlighting', whilst still working for Wilcocks. His
work was mainly of a repair, renovation or maintenance type and

he seems to have established himself as a regular supplier of services to a Mr. & Mrs. Pearce, he with a Tailors and Outfitters in Stall Street and she with a Stay Makers business in New Bond Street. Not only did he do this but Bowler also started to grow and sell vegetables and recorded the purchase of several loads of dung.[5] Bowler seems to have been an adept pupil to Nathaniel Wilcocks and was apparently held in good regard by him because, according to his business card, he became Wilcocks' foreman for ten years.

Bowler completed his apprenticeship in 1855, the year in which his first daughter, Amie Francis, was born. According to the accounts in his 'Book' he was doing an increasing amount of work in his spare time, anything it seems to increase his income – he was even exchanging work for clothing, whilst continuing his small holding which now included pigs. In 1856 his name appears in The Post Office Directory for the first time as a Gas Fitter of Villa Fields.[6]

The 1859 Directory shows Bowler still living at Villa Fields but now stated to be a Smith. In 1861 accounts appear in his 'Book' which show that he has now acquired four properties – Nos. 10, 11, 12 & 14 James Court in the Dolemeads area of Bath. He shows rents received, money spent on repairs, rates and property tax – his enterprise was beginning to pay dividends.

In the Post Office Directory for 1865 he is shown as a Brass Founder, living at 45 Villa Fields. A further set of accounts start in the same year and continue until 1869; these show more of the type of work he was carrying out which now seems to have moved principally into mineral water machinery repairs and manufacture. He noted in his 'Book': 'made a set of soda water apparatus for Sheppard, May 1865', and in 1866 'for Brookes, Bath a pump'.[7] The manufacture of these items may well have been carried out at Wilcocks because it was two years before Bowler bought a forge, anvil, tools and effects at 12 St Michaels Court, Bath, for £10.10s.0d. and two lots – a nest of drawers and steps at an auction by W.H. Brumby for 6s.6d. At this time he also bought acid, piping and lacquer, presumably in preparation for his imminent departure from Wilcocks.[8]

1869 saw him working in the manufacture of prosthetics he recorded in his book 'made a mecanicle (sic) foot and leg irons for Bell and Moody', and soon he had a licence from Bayers to make patent corset stiffeners.

By 1872 he had shown himself to be industrious and productive in other fields – he now had eleven children and had also increased his property holding by buying 1, 2, 3, 7, & 8 Petersburgh Place at Widcombe. He had also been requested to supply 24 dozen Ginger Beers to the Blathwayt Arms.

It seems not unlikely that Bowler was encouraged in his moonlighting by Wilcocks in an endeavour to rid himself of some of his smaller jobs, leaving a clear field for his larger works, and it is also very likely that he later encouraged Bowler, having witnessed his success and industry, to set up in business on his own account – they were still carrying on a working relationship after Bowler left as shown by some of the invoices in the Archive.

The Bath and West of England Manufactory for all kinds of
SODA WATER MACHINERY.

(Ten years, Foreman at the City Brass Foundry and Iron Works,)

Engineer,

PLUMBERS' AND GENERAL BRASS FOUNDER.

Gas-fitter, Lock Smith & Bell-hanger,

12, Southgate Street, BATH.

Old Brass Work Re-lacquered or Bronzed.

BRASS AND GUN METAL CASTING.

Fig.3: Bowler's Trade Card (BIHC Archive)

J B Bowler & Sons
1872-1911

It is not certain when Bowler actually left Wilcocks though his business card shows that his business was formally established in 1872. In December of that year he set up shop at No 12 Southgate Street. It was probably on the 28th of that month (bill from The Bath Gas Light and Coke Company – later one of his customers for a number of years) when he took over an area at the back of No.12 that had previously been occupied by Thomas A. Carter, Engineer. Carter was possibly retiring at that time because his name then disappears from the Bath Directories, though whether Bowler took over any stock or tools is not known.[1] The rest of No 12 Southgate Street was occupied by, and apparently owned by, Furze and Bush, Tailors, Outfitters and Undertakers to whom he paid his rent. Bowler seems to have spent a very short while getting his new premises organised because his work book starts on the 30th December where his first entry records a job at 5s.9d for Mrs Williams of Springfield Lodge for whom he had repaired a gate.[2] Monday, 6th January, shows an entry for Mr Clark's of Bridge Street for work in 'the machine room', 'repair gas pendant in workshop etc' with a total cost of 9s.0d which included man's time 8 and a half hours 6s.0d, showing that by this time he probably had an employee. The recorded costs of most of his early jobs were for relatively small amounts but, one for Brookes of Bristol – 'to repair soda water machinery' – was for £412.15s.6d which helped to push his first year's turnover to £649.4s.3d.

In January of 1873 he took delivery of 'a lathe and moulds' from

H. Brecknell of Bristol, bought for £13.0s.0d. By the middle of the year he was supplying gunmetal castings to Samuel Griffin, Millwright, this makes possible a supposition that Carter had a furnace in the workshop that Bowler took over because no mention can be found of him acquiring a furnace up to this point. Business seems to have been taking off at that point, he was still working for many of his old customers and Wilcocks was giving him repair work for mineral water machinery. Advertising in Trade Journals was producing requests for quotes on the supply of soda water machinery from all over the country, with an agent enquiring about the export of machinery to New Zealand. To one enquiry he quotes 'Large £115, small £45 (100 Doz. [bottles] per day)'.

The growth in business gave rise to a need for more capital investment and to this end Bowler decided to sell 1, 2, 3, 7 & 8 Petersburgh Place. The sale raised £150 which he used to buy stock and second hand equipment – a pump on a plank, and a pair of engines for £10.0s.0d, followed by the purchase of large quantities of new brass gas fittings and bell hanging components. A few months later, early in 1874, he continued his capital purchases buying 'a stout tub' from G. Bailey, cooper; '6 off 30lb plumbago crucibles'; 'a lathe for £12.0s.0d. from Thomas Francis' and 'the entire stock of tools and patterns in the workshop of T. Lewis, Brassfounder, Beer and Spirit Engine Manufacturer, Bell Hanger, Gas fitter etc.' – one competitor less. His turnover for the year had increased to £1,409.0s.d.

That year he received a letter, dated 24 February, from a Mr Edward James of Falfield in Gloucestershire (Bowler annotated the letter – 'near Berkley'); Mr James wrote:

Dear Sir,

I am about to start in the Mineral Water business in North America and prefer English Machinery and having been recommended to you by Mr James Smith of 42 Pleasant Street, Liverpool. I will thank you to name a day that you will be at home and at liberty to see me.

I can come to see you any day after Monday the 1st March next do not delay longer than necessary because I am limited to time, if you have a Catalogue please send me one and your reply by return.

I remain
Yours Truly
Edward James

Bowler obviously keen to do business, replied on the following day, writing:

To Mr Edward James

Feby 25th/75

Dear Sir

In answer to your kind enquiry I will remain at home on Wednesday the 3rd of March to see you unless I here (sic) from you before that time. I have no printed catalogues but shall be most happy to make any machinery that you may require also to quote you prices for the same. I have lately fitted up a large factory for a compy (sic) in Bristol.

I remain Yours etc
J B Bowler

This meeting may well have resulted in an order for a set of Mineral Water Machinery to be sent to America; costing £90. He sent it to Bristol via Gerrish & Co on a barge and then to New York on the SS *Aragon*, the cargo comprising – 3 boxes, 1 cask, and 1 wheel. This export necessitated a visit to 'The American Concel (sic) in Bristol' at a cost of 2s.6d. rail fare.[3] The visit was probably made by rail so that he could arrive looking at his best. It was apparently usual for his visits on business to be made by horse and trap or on his Velocipede.

Bowler's mother died on 9 October 1875 and the funeral arrangements were made with his landlords Furse and Bush.

In February of 1876 Bowler increased the size of his family again when his son, James Edward, was born on the 18th. He continued to receive orders and requests for information for his mineral water machinery from all over the United Kingdom, the United States of America and Australia. His customers were still increasing locally, no doubt because of his good repute. Amongst his new customers the name Annely appears on 19 February – Bowler carried out repairs and refurbishment to his existing mineral water machinery and also supplied new items.

Not all of Bowler's customers were completely satisfied however. A note from William Adams, Indian & Chinese Tea Merchant, Family Grocer, and Italian Warehouseman stated: 'Sir, I sent word last week to say your man did not make a good job of my pipe, my water has never run since.' It is interesting to note the differing forms of documents amongst the 'papers'; these vary from good quality letterheads, some with the companies' factory premises illustrated, to scraps of torn paper, an order on a piece of wallpaper and even one written on the back of a piece of sand paper.

Bowler was still receiving many requests for information and quotes for his soda water machinery; mostly he sent catalogues with a price quoted if some indication of actual requirements was stated. An exception to this was the letter he sent to Mr Aylesbury of 11 St Andrews Road, Montpelier, Bristol (Bowler kept a copy of most of his correspondence). It was a quote for the supply of soda water machinery but paints an excellent pen picture of the items involved and their installation details:

Price for a set of Soda Water Machinery as seen by yourself in Bath this day to be fixed at your premises at Bristol and left in working order, carriage of same to be paid by J B Bowler, (not including wood or stone blocks in floor, or chimney, or large water tank or pipes, for supplying same) 150 pounds net cash one half to be paid on completion of work, consisting of a oak generator with lead acid box, large copper gas holder in oak tank with pullis (sic) & balance weights, a gun metal Brahmah pattern pump in iron frame with copper solution can & copper cylinder on iron frame with water and pressure gauges & agitator, a turnover bottling machine with syruping pump, & 2 horse power steam engine with 4 horse power boiler connected with pipes, leather belts etc, awaiting your kind reply.*

> I remain, Yours Truly
> J B Bowler

Work for Annely at his Mineral Water Factory continued – it is impossible to assess whether Annely was increasing the size of his plant or that it was in such a poor condition that Bowler found complete refurbishment/renewal necessary. Annely paid all of Bowler's bills during 1876. By 1877 however, Bowler was ordering labels and stationery on behalf of Annely with whom it appears, from a later document, he had gone into partnership. Orders in the archive are still addressed to Annely and the Mineral Water business at No 2 Corn Street continued to prosper, but on 10 November of that year a document was signed by both Annely and Bowler which stated that the partnership was dissolved and that any debts of the business should be referred to Bowler who would run the business in future. What happened to Annely is not known apart from a handbill that Bowler produced which stated:

---

* Joseph Bramah was the adopted name of Joe Brammer (1748-1814) whose many inventions included a pump.

I have been informed that my late partner, Mr. W. Annely (who had a small share in my business), is now soliciting orders of my customers for Mineral Waters.

I beg to state that he has now no connection whatever in the said business, he having disposed of the same to me, and agreed not to carry on such a business in Bath except as to the manufacture of Cordials. Under these circumstances I beg to solicit continuance of the kind support I have been favoured with since I purchased the business of Mr. Thomas Bull, some two years ago; and it shall be my endeavour to merit such support by supplying all goods of first class quality.

I am,
Yours respectfully,
J. B. Bowler

Late W. Annely & Co., Manufacturers of all kinds of Cordials, Spice Extract, Ginger Ale, Lemonade, Ginger Beer, Quinine Tonic, Soda and other Mineral Waters, Corn Street Bath. Established 1864.

Oddly however, this handbill states that the business was purchased not from Annely but from Thomas Bull, though according to another handbill produced by Thomas Bull, on 14 February, 1876, he had sold his mineral water factory to W. Annely & Co. It could be postulated that Annely was deeply in debt to Bull perhaps not having paid in full for the business and that the repair and refurbishment being carried out by Bowler had left Annely in a position where he could not complete his payment to Bull and that Bull had resumed control of the business.

Bowler had also by 1877 been exhibiting his wares in London: a letter from the European Mail asks him for prospectuses for his principal exhibits which he had shown at the Aerated and Mineral Water Apparatus Exhibition at Gresham Street.

Not all was going well however: on 27 September, 1877 he received a Public Nuisance Order from the Urban Sanitary Authority for the District of Bath. The order was to remove an accumulation of dung within twenty four hours. Bowler is alleged to have claimed that it was not a nuisance, but whilst fermenting, it was providing a useful source of heating for the workshops.

He was also continuing the practice of exchanging work for goods, an invoice from his landlords shows the purchase of an overcoat for his son and for other clothes – payment by 'Contra Account'. Whilst Bowler seems to have paid his bills regularly, though often late, there are instances where he tries to give himself a discount. These produced letters suggesting, not that he was trying to cheat, but that perhaps he had misread the payment terms – he still seems to be looking for maximum profit.

It also seems likely that Bowler had begun to use Codd's Patent Globe Stoppered Bottle without a licence because a letter from Codd and Co. states that they have not yet received a reply to their letter of 13 January 1877 and 'will be glad to hear that you have decided upon taking a licence to use our patent bottles'.

Bowler seems to have driven hard bargains, though fair ones, and tried to maximise his profits in any way possible but there are no records of trouble except with one former employee. A report in the *Bath Herald* of 11 April 1881 states that Henry Hayward was charged under a warrant:

for that he did on the 2nd inst unlawfully and maliciously commit damage and spoil upon certain property, to wit certain bottles containing lemonade, horehound beer and soda water and also certain cases and tins containing biscuits and china, the property of Jonathan B. Bowler and doing damage to the sum of £2.2s ... he was drunk but not very and had threatened to burn down the premises... the prisoner stated that he had previously been in Bowler's employ but had not been able to get a reference from him ... Bowler said that he did not wish to press the charge but would like the prisoner bound over to prevent him carrying out his threat.[5]

Fig. 4: *The cottage and garden at Villa Fields with family members; Back row, left to right: Frederick Bowler, Sarah Bowler (Charlie's wife), Charlie Bowler; front row: Stanley, William (Sons of Sarah and Charlie). (Photo BIHC)*

*Right: **Map 1:** Bowler's Sites in Bath*

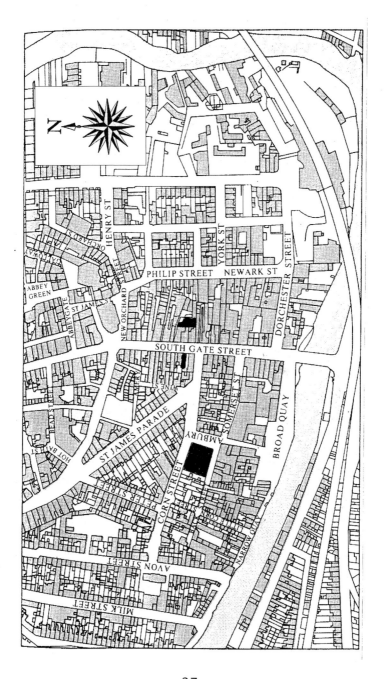

1886 saw the move of the engineering business from Southgate Street to a three-storey block of buildings in Corn Street, adjoining the mineral water factory and that year Bowler changed his residence to 4, Devonshire Terrace, Wellsway (later to become known as 205 Wellsway).

In 1882 Bowler decided to venture into the boot and shoe business, probably for one of his daughters to run, and bought stock for £500 from a Mr Milne, to start a business at No. 43 Southgate Street. A set of accounts exist for this business starting in 1882 and ending early in 1885. The accounts show that this was not one of Bowler's successful ventures – in the first fifteen weeks the income was £512.14s.2d. whilst the outgoings, which included the setting up costs, were £1175.5s.6d. This pattern continued and no doubt led to the closure of this business; the last record in the accounts was on 7 May 1885. The advertisement for the business would, no doubt, meet with disapproval these days with a little boy about to drop a rock on someone's head.

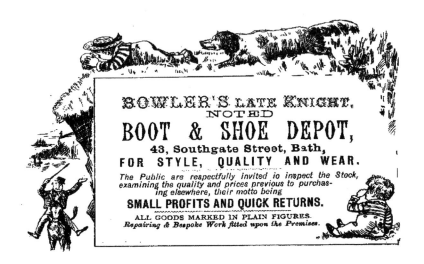

Fig. 5: *Bowler's Boots and Shoes Advertisement (BIHC Archive)*

One of Bowler's customers, Mr J. Davis, ironmonger of Walcot Street, asked if an illuminated sign could be provided outside his shop, this in the days before electricity was in general use. Bowler who never turned down any job as far as can be seen, agreed and made a sign by bending iron piping into J. Davis & Son and drilling a series of regular holes, at close intervals, in the forward facing direction. An end feed pipe was then connected to a gas supply and the gas ignited as it came through the holes. It proved to be very successful because in 1897, the year of Queen Victoria's Diamond Jubilee, the Bath Corporation asked Bowler to provide similar illuminations on the Guild Hall. It was perhaps fortunate that Bath was built of stone – the reaction of a present day fire officer leaves little to the imagination (the illumination of the Guildhall was repeated in 1902 for the Coronation of King Edward VII at a cost of £37.10s.0d.). Eventually these signs were recovered and in common with other items, in typical Bowler fashion, were retained in the workshops in case there was a future use for them. Many of the items, including the original trader's sign, are still in the collection.

Sadly Bowler's wife, Emma, died on 26 August 26 1890, at the age of fifty-five.

An undated (memo. pre-printed 190 –) memorandum from Geo. Goodman & Co of Bath (Engineers and Founders, Special Castings in soft iron, brass, gunmetal and aluminium. Brass Finishing, Patterns made accurately to drawings, lathe appliances – Models to scale. Model locomotives – Speciality, Inventors practically assisted) slated Bowler's foundry work with the following:

> *I am sorry to say that I must return all your castings, nearly everyone are full of minute holes, millions of them. You ought to cover your metal with borax or charcoal whilst melting as it absorbs air. I have offended lots of customers through these castings and consider that I have lost quite £'s. The rest are quite worthless for my purpose, & I must go elsewhere in Bristol or train a lad to do them properly, I won't have these and am very*

sorry I came to you. I owe you money about (?). I have returned
2.

Had you been able to do them <u>sound</u> I could have put any
amount of work in your way. As it is I have probably lost several
good customers not to speak of my own time.

Yours faithfully
George Goodman

It is possible that this occurred during the period of Bowler's illness when he was not carrying out his normal supervision of work.

Meanwhile the mineral water business had continued to prosper, though on a seasonal basis, increasing its turnover by selling biscuits as well. Some of the products were sold directly from the factory, but the majority were delivered by four or five roundsmen, using horse drawn carts, the horses being doubled up to cope with the load and, no doubt, the hills around Bath and the surrounding districts, including the mining area of Radstock.[6]

The business continued along much the same lines as at the start until Bowler's death in 1911 although he had continued his property acquisitions. His Last Will and Testament of 29 June 1911, whilst living at 205, Wellsway, listed his property assets as:

<u>Ground Rent / Rent Charge</u>

53, 54, 55, Herbert Road,
2, 3, 4, 5 Little Corn Street
2, New Quay,
17, 18, 19, 21, 22, 23, 27, Livingstone Road,
10, 11, Somerset Street,
11, Morford Street,
(?) Whitakers Buildings, (?) Bristol.

Messuages and Premises

5, The Ambury
12, 12a, 12b, Balon (?) Road
11, Belgrave Crescent
12, 13, Corn Street
15, 16, Corn Street (& adjoining warehouse)
8, Second Avenue, King Edward Road
1, Corn StreetPlace (& stables, yard & workshops & the hayloft in Back St.)
2, Corn StreetPlace
Lower Stirtingdale Lane, Sladebrook (?) Estate, Englishcombe (with wooden and other houses in connection with aerated water business).

Fig. 6: Jonathan Bowler in the 1900s (BIHC Archive).

Bowler died on 9 March, 1911, at the age of seventy-seven, and at that time the company had twenty-four employees. His will was probated at Bristol on 29 June, 1911, to Charles Moody Bowler, Brass Founder and Graham Simmons, Solicitor. The probate value was £10,214.14s.1d.[7] In 1990s figures, using Bank of England RPI figures for 1993, about £409,000.

Bowler's thirteen children all survived infancy, which was fairly unusual in Victorian times and were all alive at the time of his death.[8] His children were as follows:

Amie Francis	b. 21 August 1855
Kate Emma	b. 1 December 1857
Louisa Mary	b. 20 August 1858
Frederick Burdett	b. 22 January 1860
Charles Moody	b. 4 October 1861
William Woodman	b. 4 May 1863
Frank John	b. 12 January 1865
Ellen Caroline	b. 10 October 1866
Hannah Penton	b. 28 August 1868
George Thomas	b. 9 March 1870
Fanny Ada	b. 9 November 1871
Robert Douglas	b. 18 August 1873
James Edward	b. 10 February 1876

Fig. 7: Twelve of the thirteen children; back row, left to right: Hannah Penton, George, Katherine Emma, Frank John, Ellen Caroline; Middle row: Amy Francis, Charles Moody, Louisa Mary, William Woodman, Fanny Ada; Front row: Robert Douglas, James Edward.

The fact that all of his children survived infancy must to some extent show that Bowler's industry had provided a standard of living for his family which was well above the norm for that period when infant mortality was high.

Ernest Bowler, J B Bowler's grandson, who was the final manager of the businesses, took part in a taped interview in 1972 and tells of early memories of his grandfather and the later years of the business:

He was fair but firm, respected by his children and the employees and known as 'the Governor'....He was a man of few words but always got his point across...Until he had a stroke, in his later years, he would arrive early at the factory and leave late, having taken a substantial tea above the workshops with his sons, the tea having been prepared by his daughters who worked in the mineral water factory...After his stroke he slowed down and arrived from his house in Wellsway by Tram at about 9 am...He still stayed very late and took tea, but the trap was called to take him home again...Following his death in 1911 a limited company was formed to run the business but from that time on the company seemed to go along relying on reputation rather than looking for new things to do and waited for people to come to them.[9]

YEAR	1873	1881	1886	1891	1896	1901	1906	1911
£ actual	649	1409	1177	1523	1258	1312	1767	3052
£ (1990s)	22715	53542	52969	65489	60384	59040	79515	125132

Table 1: Engineering Turnover 1873-1911

YEAR	1889	1890	1891	1901	1910
£ actual	1500	1618	1744	1586	1523
£ (1990s)	67500	69574	83712	71820	62443

Table 2: Mineral Water Turnover 1889-1910

𝔐emorandum of 𝔄ssociation

AND

𝔄rticles of 𝔄ssociation

OF

J. B. BOWLER & SONS,

LIMITED.

*Above: **Fig. 8** Memorandum of Association*

*Below: **Fig. 9** Memorandum of Association*

3.   The objects for which the Company is established are :—

(*a*) To carry on the business of Engineers and Brassfounders and all allied trades also the business of Mineral Water Manufacturers and all allied trades whether on the Company's own account or under any contract with other persons.

(*b*) As a first operation of the Company to acquire and take over as a going concern the engineering and brassfounding business now carried on by Charles Moody Bowler Frank John Bowler George Thomas Bowler Robert Douglas Bowler and Edward James Bowler. And also to acquire and take over as a going concern the Mineral Water Manufacturers' business now carried on by William Woodman Bowler Hannah Penton Spurway and Fanny Ada Bowler at Corn Street Bath and elsewhere under the style of **J. B.** Bowler & Sons with the stock-in-trade plant machinery tools and general effects of the business upon the terms with or without modifications of an Agreement dated the Seventh day of October 1911 and made between the said Charles Moody

34

J B Bowler & Sons Ltd
1911-1969

In January of 1911, the year of Jonathan Bowler's death, the cashbook shows a Bank Balance of £1,150.0s.10d. During the year the business continued to prosper to the extent that the heirs decided to give themselves a Christmas bonus. Cash entries show that ten members, of the family firm, were paid the following sums:

C M Bowler	£120.00s.0d	R D Bowler	£82.10s.0d
W W Bowler	£82.10s.0d	E J Bowler	£82.10s.0d
F J Bowler	£82.10s.0d	G T Bowler	£82.10s.0d
H P Spurway	£60.00s.0d	F A Bowler	£60.00s.0d
E Carpenter	£7.07s.0d	A W Wills	£5.00s.0d

In 1911, following Bowler's death, the family decided to form a limited liability company and an article to that effect was signed on 7 October 1911.[1] During the year Cash In was £3,089.00s.0d. and Cash Out £1,835.11s.5d. giving a surplus of £1,253.08s.7d. on the years' trading. Charles Moody Bowler had become Managing Director of the Company and was running the engineering side, whilst William Woodman Bowler was running the mineral water business. Charles, or Charlie, (many documents are addressed to Mr. Charlie or Charlie) as he was generally known, had taken charge, as second eldest son, in the absence of his older brother, Frederick, who had emigrated to the United States of America, and of whom little more is known.

The turnover in this year saw a considerable increase which

possibly demonstrates either that the business had to a certain extent suffered since Bowler's stroke and failing health, the likelihood is that patriarchal control made it impossible to expand further because Bowler was still the 'Governor'[2]: or that the books were not being managed as previously. Work continued as before in the new limited company though things were not always straightforward – an invoice from Edward Foster & Sons Ltd on 10 April 1912 had a red sticker attached stating:

> 'Coal Strike The Railway and Shipping Companies advise us that at present they cannot guarantee deliveries, and we are therefore compelled to advise customers that we do not accept responsibility for delay or loss in transit.'

And on 28 November 1913 a bill was received for David Adams' funeral. Was this an employee who had died and the company had paid for his funeral? No record of his name appears in the books apart from a George Adams who was the leading hand in the foundry.

At the back of an Income and Expenditure daybook an undated inventory was found. It covers the whole of the Bowler factory premises and lists all items found therein. Very possibly the inventory was used in the probate of Bowler's Will. It is certainly fairly early because long S's are used in some entries. Listed were the contents and tools of:

The Mineral Water Factory	Large Machine Shop .
The Small Shop	The Smiths Shop
The Dipping Shop	Over the Dipping Shop
The Foundry	The Old Dipping Shop
In the Bake House	The Lacquering Room
The Pattern Room	The Brass shop
The Ambury	The Ambury Front Room
The Ambury No 2 Room	The Ambury No 3 Room
The Top Room	The Corner Shop - Front Room
The Warehouse - Top Room	

By 1914 Bath City Council had adopted a 'Fair Wage Clause' and on the top of an order received by Bowlers is a sticker stating that 'this order is subject to traders agreeing to comply with that clause'. Officialdom seems to have been largely ignored by Charlie Bowler in 1914 – on 6 April an Income Tax return was sent, on 29 April an Income Tax reminder had been sent, there is an unopened letter from the Collector of Taxes which had been sent on 25 May, and on 10 July there was a reminder that a Board of Trade census form had not been returned. Then on 9 December a letter was sent on general business circulation from The Board of Trade (Labour Exchanges and Unemployment Department) thanking employers for their co-operation in completing their census returns but enclosing a final reminder for Bowler – several other official letters had been received during the year. In September, The Board of Trade (Commercial Intelligence Branch) had also circulated all businesses suggesting that traders should try to take advantage of the war to get into neutral and colonial markets in which the Germans and Austrians had previously had a large trade.

During the war years, although some staff had been lost to war service (the twenty employees in 1914 were down to thirteen by 1917, according to the wages book for that period) Bowlers were becoming more and more involved with the emergent motor trade supplying nuts, bolts, and paint and doing general repairs for the garage trade. Among their customers were The Aeolus Motor Manufacturing and Horstman Motor and Gear Companies. The war also brought increased trade with Bath Cabinet Makers and their war time associate The Bath Aeroplane Company.[3]

They were also indirectly involved with the war effort in supplying goods and services to customers whose letterheads were overstamped 'Contractors to the War Office and Admiralty' or 'Under Government Control' this witnessed by a Ministry of Munitions Certificate, from Horstman Gear & Co Ltd., for 'the priority supply of American steel bar'. Either due to pressure of work from these Companies or due to shortage of staff some of the pattern making was contracted out to The Bath Cabinet Makers.[4]

The war years saw the output from the mineral water factory reduced due to restrictions on sugar supply and, in 1916, a licensing system was introduced by the Ministry of Supply with the licence headed 'The Manufacture for Sale of Table Waters' at a fee of 10s. per annum – Bowlers seem to have anticipated this and bought additional supplies in 1915 and 1916.[5] Later in the war the supply of sulphuric acid for the carbon dioxide generator became difficult and 'Tubes' of carbon dioxide were purchased from The Bristol Distilling Company.[6]

Bowler's major customers during the war years of 1914 to 1918 were:

Aeolus Engineering	*Engineers*
Aldridge and Ranken	*Engineers*
Bath Cabinet Makers	*Aeroplanes*
Bath Aeroplane Company	*Aeroplanes*
Bath Cold Storage & Ice Co	
Bath Corporation Electricity Co	
Bath Gas Light & Coke Co	
Bath Electric Tramways	
Bath Engineering Company	*Engineers*
Bath Steam Haulage Co	
Bath Water Company	
Bladwells	*Eng. & Plumbing Supplies*
Royal Spa, Grand Pump Room, Empire	*Hotels*
Horstmann Car Company	*Engineers*
Horstmann Gear Company	*Engineers*
Kingswood School	
Bath Steam, Bath Hygienic, Bath Original	*Laundries*
Robert Membery	*Eng. & Plumbing Supplies*
Royal School for the Daughters of Army Officers	

Stanley Engineering	*Engineers*
Walcot Foundry	*Engineers*
Walter J. Coward	*Engineers*

One of the Account Books / Day Books which exists for the periods 1916-1922 and 1960-1964 seemed to relate to a possible drapery business in the early period and the engineering business in the latter. Most of the entries for the 1917-1922 period of the Day Book refer to drapery items or to items apparently involved in the setting up of a shop – a further consideration of these items, which included a drawing room suite and carpet for sitting room made the drapery business seem less viable. The first entry appeared on 19 March 1917.

An examination of the accounts revealed that, in April 1920, a bill for 10s.3d. was settled, in favour of J B Bowler & Sons, work not specified. A check on Bowler's books for the same item showed that it was paid by Miss Dagger of Gay Street. This led to a search in the Post Office Directories for possible businesses in Gay Street in the appropriate years. No drapers were found but several dressmakers and costumiers, these included a Madame Alyce - Costumier, and further reference to the accounts saw mention of Madame Alyce and the purchase of fashion books. There is also an item in the book for 'carriage of dresses 2/-'.

The premises were rented from The River's Estate and the rent was paid to Miss Eleanor Blackburn for The River's Estate which in turn paid the rates.[8] It was not clear who owned the business or how the book came to be in Bowler's possession but, according to Bowler's Book, two of his daughters, Amey and Kate, were apprenticed to a dressmaker in Queen Square in 1870; was one of these daughters Madame Alyce having taken a more grand name to impress her customers? What is clear, however, is that the business was not a good one. An analysis of the accounts on a crude basis, i.e. Cash in / Cash Out, and taking no account of stock or assets, which are impossible to assess, is shown below:

Year	Cash in	Cash out	Loss
1917	£134.11s.8d.	£179.09s.9d.	£44.10s.1d.
1918	£335.13s.9d.	£366.16s.4d.	£41.06s.5d.
1919	£506.03s.7d.	£550.01s.5d.	£74.08s.1d.
1920	£522.06s.0d.	£704.19s.7d.	£182.13s.6d.
1921	£366.07s.1d.	£309.14s.3d.	£56.12s.9d.
1922	£152.08s.4d.	£202.06s.8d.	£49.10s.4d.
1922	£152.08s.4d.	£202.06s.8d.	£49.10s.4d.

The first employee, possibly the manageress, is shown to be a Miss E Dagger and she continued to receive wages right through to the end of the account having been joined by Miss Street, Miss Harding and Miss Hillier as the business progressed. In April 1918 a cash sum is mentioned for the placing of an advertisement but where the advert is to be placed is not stated. In 1919 three advertisements are placed, the third in the Macdonalds Directory, perhaps the losses are beginning to cause concern. 1920 saw further advertisements including one in the Somerset directory, though by this time business must have been brisk, if not profitable, because an errand boy was shown as receiving wages of 8 shillings.

A check through the customers showed that a Mrs Bowler had visited the shop on six occasions and Mrs C. Bowler once - the same lady? Miss Blackburn was also a customer and Miss N Dagger perhaps Miss E Dagger's sister. Madame Alyce's main suppliers with whom she had accounts were: Colmers, Ealand & Sons, Lyons & Co., Jolly & Sons, Evans & Owens, Walker & Ling, and Harris & Newman

A letter to the *Bath Chronicle* for information regarding Madame Alyce produced a response from a Mr Frank Ludlow. He knew of the business and said that Alyce was pronounced Aleese so that it sounded 'a bit grander'. The letter continues: 'The business was run by Miss Elsie Dagger, who never looked very smart for a Costumier, though she seemed to advertise the business by dressing her sister, Nora, up to a high standard to demonstrate – 'this is what

I can do'. The Daggers had been his neighbours at Powlett Road, he at No 11a and they at No 10a, their father was an engineer working at Stothert and Pitt. 'The family were friendly but always seemed to think they were a cut above the average. They were very friendly with the Bowlers, Mr Dagger and Charlie were very close. Eventually the business moved to much smaller premises – an annexe to the Post Office on the corner of Bathwick Streetand Daniel Street'. It seems quite possible that Bowlers may have helped in the move and acquired the account book then. Never known to waste anything, they used the rest of the book for their own business.

A man-hour record is at the back of the shoe business accounts book – any abandoned book that had spare pages always seemed to be re-used for something else (though surprisingly, there is a completely unused ledger in the collection). This details time spent on making a brass crane for Stothert and Pitt with man-hours shown for Ted, G, E, C, and Boy's time, probably mostly Bowler's sons. It had by this time become a family business with nearly all the family seeming to be involved. The record runs from May to October but the year is not shown. Fortunately, two of the day entries, most of which were shown as Monday, Tuesday etc. had an actual day of month against them. Using a 'retro' calendar the year was established as 1924. Time spent was 1,484 hours of man's time and 1,484 hours of boy's time, mostly at seventy hours per week each.

The letter sent to the *Bath Chronicle* re Madame Alyce, (see page 40) resulted in an interview with Mr Frank Ludlow, eighty-eight years old, and the former General Manager of Duck Son & Pinker Ltd (an account customer of Bowlers for many years). He asked if anything had been discovered about the Brass Cranes which he remembered being displayed in Bowler's shop window – 'it was a model of a Stothert & Pitt crane and was used by them to send to prospective customers as advertising material, many of them were displayed in Bowler's shop window'. They were about eight or nine inches tall from his memory. The date was probably early 1920's.

A further letter to the *Bath Chronicle*, asking for information on any surviving model cranes brought a response from Mrs Joan Day who said that she had a photograph of four model cranes which had been in the possession of her late father. Mrs Day's father, who died in 1930, was Charles Gibbs, known to his friends as Charlie and had been a toolmaker at the Horstman Gear Company. The photograph was shown to Mr Ludlow who confirmed that the cranes seemed to be the same as those he had seen in Bowler's window though, with the passage of time, absolute identification could not be certain.

Many of the skilled engineering workers in Bath were probably known to each other, maybe from apprenticeship days, and would certainly be interested in seeing any special projects which had been worked on. This may account for Charlie Gibb's possession of the photograph.

Fig. 10: *The Brass Cranes (Photograph courtesy of Joan Day).*

Business seems to have quickly resumed as normal after the war though Bowlers' letterhead shows that they were now the main agents for Cryselco Lamps, having changed from main agents for Premier Accumulators. Once again gas illuminations were fitted to the Guildhall, this time to celebrate the end of the Great War. The previous activities were continuing but by 1925 an invoice shows that Bowlers were no longer just assisting others in the motor industry with repairs. The invoice, from builders F J Drake, refers to pinning up steel joist over entrance to sliding doors at The Motor Works, Ambury. A letter in the same year to T Hood and Company of Queens Road, Bristol, is about a failed back axle from a Crouch car, which they had taken down and discovered to have been incorrectly assembled, this causing its failure. January 17, 1925 brought a cheque for £1.14s.0d. from the Official Receiver in respect of Horstmann Cars which had demised.

By 1930 there is no further mention of the Motor Works but Bowlers were still dealing with the motor repairs trade supplying Ferodo brake linings and other items. Invoices show that they were buying petrol – 2/300 gallons per month from British Petroleum. Cooks ordered 1 Doz electric lamps, 110 volts, 60 candle power. William Crawford supplied biscuits for the mineral water factory and Dawson & Sons billed them for £224 for setting Lancashire Boiler at Oldfield Park Laundry. The tone of requests to do work had moderated by this time – a letter from the Circus Tavern says

Dear Mr Bowler, Could you come and see to one of my engines, it is leaking rather badly. Could you manage it today? I should be glad if you could.

Yours truly,
A.N.Mills

This letter was annotated Fussell & Sons, Circus Brewery.

Charles Bowler in that year paid an insurance premium on an 8 hp Rover car valued at £50, and the company was carrying out a lot of work for various water companies providing fencing and chequer plates. There was also a bill of £1.12s.6d. from B Roberts

43

and Co. Ltd., advertising agents of Leicester Square, for an advertisement on the curtain of the Theatre Royal. The company had also started buying Smith's Crisps and were selling vinegar. Engineering plant was also increased with the purchase of a turret lathe (by Herbert & Sons of Coventry) for £6, bought in a sale, ex-Western Counties Haulage – Jonathan Bowler's practice of buying items at auctions and sales both for use in the workshops and for re-sale was still a regular part of the company's activities.

It seems by now that Bowlers were doing less work in their workshops and had become suppliers of practically everything in the general engineering, metal, public house and brewery hardware, plumbing, heating, and electrical line. They were still carrying out work for customers almost regardless of what was involved, eg. the refurbishment of the Cleveland Bridge in Bath and even painting and decorating – if they couldn't do it they knew a man who could. An invoice for 10 shillings showed that C Hooper, Patternmaker, made a pattern and core box and on 8 April, Thomas Cook & Sons,

***Fig.11**: The Corn Street premises in the 1930's (BIHC Archive)*

Victoria Coach Works, made and fitted a new hood for the 8 hp Rover at a cost of £2.9s.6d.

The Eezit Company, which had previously traded from Linden Road in Bristol had moved to 31 Park Grove, Henleaze, Bristol. This locally made product was very popular in the engineering and motor repair industries as was demonstrated by the quantities which Bowlers' ordered. Stubborn or rusted nuts were often very easily freed by the application of Eezit (the WD 40 of the 1930's?).

In 1935, Bowlers' vanman had an accident, involving a cycle, and they paid the bill for repairs (7 shillings) to Vic Anstice, Motorcycle Specialist of Westgate Buildings, Bath. A final reminder was received in March 1936 for their Electricity Bill that should have been paid in the previous December.

Scrap was still being bought; an invoice from The Royal School, Bath for 10 shillings is for the purchase of a scrap potato machine. Many of the scrap items they bought were renovated and resold at a profit. Petrol was still being bought at the same rate but Shell Mex and British Petroleum had amalgamated.

Very few papers are filed for this period, but an account customers work book shows some of the outside work undertaken in 1940/41/42. The year 1940 must have had a very cold beginning because the first entries for January and February show repairs to thirty burst water pipes and several burst flushing tanks. They were still involved with the motor trade - Marlborough Lane Garage was billed 2 shillings for 'taking down exhaust and silencer on Rover car with your man'. In February and March of that year they overhauled the Bath Hygienic Laundry's air raid siren and then 'excavated ground and erected concrete air raid shelters providing retaining walls, sandbags and emergency lighting'. The laundry and Bath Electric Light Company were their two best customers for that year.

By 1941 the Bath Hygienic Laundry must have been short of staff, possibly due to war service, because Bowler's were providing 'an acting maintainance (sic) engineer and mate' and then an 'acting stoker'. This continued for several periods throughout the year. In

45

July they repaired two brass musical instruments for the Air Training Corps and also the siren at the Bath Electric Light Company. Bath Victoria Brick & Tile Company appear in the accounts several times. April 1942 sees the first evidence of war damage with an entry for work at Mr Sing Lee's Laundry reading 'not done Blitzed'.

The mineral water business had changed in that Bowlers were now buying in Britvic bottled drinks in flavours of tomato, orange, grapefruit, and pineapple from British Vitamin Products Ltd of Chelmsford, Essex. They were also buying casks of cider from H P Bulmer of Hereford. Their own manufactury continued but possibly customer demand for nationally known products had brought about this change.

July 1955 showed an invoice from Bowlers to Bath City Football Club for soft drinks. The invoice is receipted but, for the first time seen in the collection, there is an auditors' stamp stating that the document has been seen by the auditors – Ham, Jackson & Brown, Chartered Accountants.

Later in the year more drinks were bought in, this time Lucozade, Ribena & Quosh from Beecham Foods of Brentford, Middlesex. They also bought crisps from Minster Pre Pack Foods of Wimborne.

Evidence that they were no longer doing motor repairs is provided by an invoice from Western Counties Automobile Co. Ltd., of 46 Walcot Street, Bath, for the repair of their Bedford KD, Registration BFB 424 - fix brakes. Teign Cider supplied twenty-four and a half gallons of Applecham. Meanwhile the engineering business continued as before.

Bowlers 'stopped the clock' in their Day Book on Wednesday 20 November, 1963. The entry for that day reads 'Cancelled Flooding'.

An invoice from the Carborundum Co Ltd., is overstamped – 'Cheques Act 1957 – we do not issue receipts unless requested'. Engineering sales were still continuing with items ranging from carborundum powder, nuts and bolts, taps and dies, lengths of steel, copper and aluminium bar to boilers.

In June of 1965, 1,183 10oz, square-shoulder, ginger beer bottles with crown mouths were bought from Price, Powell & Co. of Southville Bristol at a cost of £36.19s.5d. delivered by British Rail; the freight charge that was included in the price amounted to a surcharge of 5% or £1.17s. Price & Powell wrote again on 20 March 1961, saying that in the interests of economy and efficiency they were closing the Bristol premises and would in future operate from Chesterfield. That was about the time when the rationalisation of businesses started in the 1960's and has never stopped since. Orders from the former Ministry of Works show that it is now the Ministry of Public Building and Works.

There are few papers filed around these dates and apparently most of the final year papers were taken by the accountants or solicitors winding up the Company. Nothing at all is filed from 1967 onward.

It could probably be said, without exaggeration, that most of the population of Bath, either directly or indirectly via other tradesmen, were Bowler's customers at some time. However, those customers which appear most frequently in the records are traders and those of the traders making the most purchases in the 1930's are recorded below: Bath Hygienic Laundry; Hayward & Wooster Ltd.; Bath Electricity Department; Horstmann Gear Co. Ltd.; Bathite Ltd., Combe Down; Horstmann Ltd.; Bath Waterworks; Kingsmead Motor Co.; Cary and Sons, Twerton; J Long & Sons; Commercial Garage, Palace Mews; Robert Membery; Erwood & Morris, Railway Place; The Royal School, Lansdown; Foster & Sons; Ambury, Rickards, Trunk Maker; Forbes Fraser Hospital; Stothert & Pitt Co Ltd.; S & A Fullers Ltd, Kingsmead St.; Stockall & Sons; G. Glisson, Milk St.; Stanley Engineering Co Ltd.; Gayner & Sons, Julian Rd.; Shellard, City Steam Transport; Harding & Co, Invalid Chair Makers.

Those in the 1960's were: A. G Workman; Horstmann Ltd.; Avon Rubber Co Ltd.; Ministry Of Works; Bath Cabinet Makers Ltd.; Nitro Liquor; Bath & Portland Stone; Sainsbury Bros.; Bath Panel Beating; South Western Electricity Board; C-I-C Engineering; South West Gas; Fortts; Rotork Engineers; Frankcombe Engineering; Walters

Engineering Co. Ltd.; G. W. Sparrow; Whitby Motors.

YEAR	1916	1921	1931	1937
£ actual	3242	4490	3930	2806
£ (1990s)	81050	76330	98250	75762

Table 3: Engineering Turnover 1916-1937

YEAR	1931	1948	1951	1954	1962
£ actual	1516	2512	3606	4562	6467
£ (1990s)	37900	47728	64908	59306	77604

Table 4: Mineral Water Turnover 1931-1937

The figures used in the preparation of these Tables are the only ones available from the archive books.

Fig 12: Ernest Bowler, the final manager of the business
(BIHC Archive)

TRADE / YEAR	1783	1784	1787	1791	1800	1805	1809	1812	1819	1822
Aerated Water Manf	*0*	*0*	*0*	*0*	*0*	*0*	*0*	*0*	*0*	*0*
Bellhanger	0	0	0	0	1	2	4	0	2	0
Bk'smiths & Smiths	0	0	0	6	5	10	5	6	18	8
Brass Founder	0	0	0	1	0	0	0	0	0	1
Brazier	4	3	6	7	3	1	4	2	3	3
Bright&Whitesmiths	0	0	0	0	4	5	9	4	8	6
Coppersmith	0	0	0	0	0	0	1	0	0	0
Engineer	0	0	0	0	0	0	2	1	4	1
Gas Fitter	0	0	0	0	0	0	0	0	0	0
Iron Founder	0	0	0	0	0	0	0	0	1	0
Locksmith	0	0	0	0	0	3	3	2	3	2
Millwright	0	0	0	0	1	0	1	0	1	1
Plumber	0	0	1	3	11	5	10	8	13	11
Tinman	2	2	0	1	6	3	4	2	1	3
Zinc Worker	0	0	0	0	0	0	0	0	0	0
Total	6	5	7	18	31	29	43	25	54	36

Table 5: Metal Trade Occupations, 1783-1824

Bowler's Associated Trades in Bath
1783-1866

The Metal Trades

Jonathan Burdett Bowler, having become an apprentice in 1848, had joined a Bath workforce which was steadily increasing its numbers, with the types of trades which he eventually claimed on his trade card growing rapidly. To determine the rate of growth of the various metal industry trades in Bath, and where their primary locations were to be found, a database was constructed using the Bath Street Directories, 1783-1866, and reports produced with the entries sorted by trade and address.[1] Aerated water manufacturers were also entered and are included in Tables 5 & 6 for information, but not counted in the Totals. The later directories covered a much larger area than the immediate environs of Bath, taking in villages as far away as Marshfield, but these locations were excluded from the database.

The early directories are very small and undoubtedly do not reflect either the true population of Bath or indeed the correct number of people involved in the trades tables produced. They do however demonstrate the growth in those trades and the increasing demands of the population for those products produced by the metal and engineering trades generally. It was not until the Directories were taken over by the Post Office, from 1858, that some consistency in their preparation becomes obvious. What is not certain, in all cases, is whether work was carried on at the addresses quoted or whether they were residences only – in some cases two addresses are given, one as the trade address and one for the residence (the residence was not listed). However, a pattern of the working areas still emerges.

TRADE / YEAR	1826	1829	1830	1833	1837	1841	1846	1850	1856	1860	1866
Aerated Water Manf	0	0	0	0	0	1	0	0	2	1	4
Bellhanger	3	4	1	1	2	4	2	6	12	11	7
Bk'Smiths&Smiths	22	34	6	6	13	29	31	19	73	64	89
Brass Founder	3	7	3	3	2	3	3	3	6	6	4
Brazier	3	5	1	2	2	3	2	11	0	3	2
Bright&Whitesmiths	11	12	8	8	8	9	11	12	8	7	9
Coppersmith	0	1	3	3	1	1	1	0	0	0	0
Engineer	0	1	2	2	3	9	3	11	19	33	32
Gas Fitter	0	0	0	0	0	0	0	3	15	21	31
Iron Founder	1	3	2	2	2	2	1	1	2	2	2
Locksmith	4	5	3	3	2	3	4	8	9	9	5
Millwright	2	3	2	2	1	2	1	8	3	3	10
Plumber	13	21	22	20	19	14	19	18	33	34	27
Tinman	5	3	2	2	3	5	5	8	8	8	15
Zinc Worker	0	0	0	0	0	0	3	4	2	2	2
Total	**67**	**99**	**55**	**54**	**58**	**84**	**86**	**112**	**190**	**203**	**235**

Table 6*: Metal Trade Occupations, 1826-1860*

Another problem in determining the numerical quantities of the various trades is the change of job title which some have shown, though probably doing much the same work, or perhaps this was an inconsistency by the directory compilers because sometimes, where there is a separate trade directory section, the description shown there differs from the description in the main directory. To demonstrate this a database report was produced where the entries were sorted by name showing how their trade description varied over the years. For example, in 1791 Bishop & Dyke were shown as smiths but by 1800 they had become braziers. It can be argued though that some did advance in their trades – for example many millwrights who were skilled in both carpentry, metalworking, building and more, did change their trade description to Engineer. This was, in many cases, before the title chartered engineer or professional engineer had formally begun its use, with the formation of professional bodies requiring qualifications to obtain membership or associate membership of their professional engineering body.

Many of the people claiming the title of Engineer were probably not educated to the required standard, but could certainly have held their own with anyone entitled to the professional status of Engineer. In many cases they were self taught and their engineering achievements were the result of instinctive or empirical methods.

The Institution of Civil Engineers was founded in 1818 – these Engineers having originated mainly from the people required by the military for the construction of their fortifications. The title Civil Engineer was defined as any engineer in civil, as distinct from military, employment and comprised in general the builders of canals, new roads, bridges and harbours.

The Mechanical Engineer did not really emerge until after the Industrial Revolution which had produced much innovation and invention of mechanical products, the most important being the steam engine, all of which led on to the present day when society without machines would be unimaginable. It was also well before the advent of mass production so that machines were basically produced on a 'one-off' basis giving rise to 'one-off' repairs: a tremendous opportunity for those with the required engineering bent. The Institution of Mechanical Engineers and therefore the qualification M.I.Mech.E. or A.M.I.Mech.E. was formed in 1847, having broken away from the civil engineers, most notably by the new locomotive men.[2]

The Locations of those in the Metal Trades

The addresses which appear most frequently and thus indicate concentrations of activity are listed in Table 7; the entries are cumulative. Horse Street had by 1866 been taken into Southgate Street and the figures for the two have been added together. Not surprisingly, perhaps, the largest concentrations were found to be close to the banks of the River Avon. The largest concentration being around the Quay on the north side of the river and forming a rough rectangle bounded by the Quay, Milk Street up to Borough Walls and then back down to the river via Southgate, Philip and Newark

Streets: the latter three streets taking in the Newark Foundry of Stothert & Pitt. On the north side of this rectangle there was apparently a sharp social cut off between trade and gentility – when Ernest Bowler was interviewed, regarding boyhood days, he said 'Oh no we couldn't go up into Milsom Street, unless we were on our best behaviour, it was a place apart, we'd get chased off. They had old men who swept the road, so that the ladies could cross, because it wasn't made up like it is now, the roads were muddy'.[3] Across the river on its southern side there were also fairly large groups around Beechen Cliff, Claverton Street, Claverton Buildings and Holloway which had forty-seven appearances – the most seen. Moving towards the Lower Bristol Road the block formed by Westmoreland Buildings, Oak Street and Wood Street also showed a fairly large group populated by engineers, millwrights, tinmen, an iron founder and also George Rayno, who in 1826 was shown as a millwright. Rayno had joined Stothert and Pitt as a partner to form Stothert, Rayno & Pitt, but due to ill health was forced to leave the partnership in 1855 when the firm reverted again to Stothert & Pitt. The company had become recognised as good quality engineers and ironfounders and were employed by Brunel to assist with materials and pumps for his Great Western Railway which had reached Bath from Bristol in 1840 and then on towards London opening fully in 1841.[4]

Another large, but strung out group of the associated trades followed the course of the river along Walcot Street into Walcot and then on to the London Road. More were to be found at Twerton where the cloth industry was concentrated.

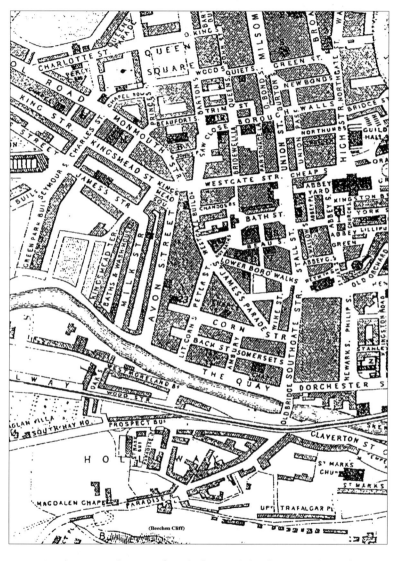

Map 2: *The central area of Bath from Philips' Street Plan of 1856*

Abbey Green	10	Little Corn Street	2
Abbey Street	1	Lower Borough Walls	12
Abbey Yard	1	Milk Street	8
Avon Street	14	New Bond Street	4
Back Street	6	Newark Street	5
Beechen Cliff	22	Oak Street	17
Borough Walls	13	Old Orchard Street	1
Bridewell Lane	37	Orange Grove	7
Bristol Road	23	Philip Street	10
Charlotte Street	7	Princes Street	16
Cheap Street	7	Southgate Street	27
Claverton Street	21	Stall Street	9
Corn Street	19	Trim Street	4
Green Street	3	Union Passage	1
Holloway	47	Westgate Street	22
James Street	16	Westmoreland Buildings	9
Kingsmead Square	7	Wine Street	8
Kingsmead Street	18	Wood Street	6
Kingsmead Terrace	3	York Street	3

***Table 7**: Directory appearances of metal trades addresses, (central area)*

River trade from around the Quay area of the city began when the first part of the Kennet & Avon Canal – the Avon Navigation – was opened up in 1727, giving Bath access to the then prosperous port of Bristol, the River Severn and South Wales and to cheap water-borne goods. Attempts had previously been made to open up this navigation but the obstruction by weirs, which had been provided to operate the various mills en route to Bristol, and resistance to their removal by their owners had proved an insoluble problem until, in 1712, Bath Corporation managed to get a Parliamentary Bill passed to enable the Navigation. Eventually, in 1810, the Navigation was linked with a canal towards London forming the Kennet and Avon

Canal.[5] The provision of the canal no doubt led to more smith work; the horses towing the barges would have needed shoeing, and cargo handling and transportation would certainly have led to more work for the metal trades.

The trade of bellhanger was growing because, for many, the door knocker was no longer fashionable and it did mean that in the larger houses with servants the front door bell could be made to ring, via a pulled wire, in the servants quarters; servants could also be summoned to any room fitted with a bell caller. Many smaller houses were also fitted with wire-operated front door bells. Not only bellhangers benefited from the trade; the requirement for wire, bells, bell cranks to negotiate corners and handles or pulls to operate the bells led to more work for the brass founders and finishers.

In 1818 the Bath Gas Light Company was formed to produce town gas; henceforth gas lighting, both public and domestic, benefited the population.[6] This was followed by the Bath Waterworks Act of 1846 which led to a gradually increasing need for plumbing work as the supply of mains water to domestic and other premises began.[7] Another opportunity for those with the necessary skills to develop their businesses and this again, of course, led to more work for the brass founders in producing the required fittings.

The brass trade also found that brewers and publicans had need of their beer engines and other pumps and fittings. Overall, it was a good time to be starting a business.

YEAR	Bath	Weston	Twerton
1801	34160	1010	764
1811	38434	1291	1111
1821	46688	1919	1500
1831	50809	2560	2478
1841	53209	2899	3342
1851	54248	3082	2959
1861	52533	3127	3012
1871	52569	3570	3634

Table 8: The growth in population 1801-1871

Bath was also slowly increasing its indigenous population (Table 8 shows the increase from 1801-1871) though this was not a completely linear change – the population peaked in 1851 then fell back again to resume a gradual increase, Added to this, fairly large numbers of visitors were still coming to Bath to 'take the waters', though tailing off in the latter years, resulting in an increasing requirement for service industries.

The population numbers in Table 8 were obtained from the National Census of Population figures and for Bath covers the parishes of St. Peter and St. Paul, St. James, St. Michael, Walcot, Bathwick, plus Lyncombe and Widcombe after 1830. Weston and Twerton show fairly rapid growth, stemming particularly from the growth in the weaving and clothing manufacturing industries – these again, of course, requiring the metal workers' engineering skills.

Aerated Water Manufacture
Aerated water was not produced on a commercial basis until Jean Jacob Schweppe produced an apparatus for the carbonation of water by using a mechanical pump.[8]

Schweppe was born in Witzenhausen in Germany in 1740 and was put to work with a tinker. The tinker found his dexterity such that he considered Schweppe wasted on such a trade and recommended that he be placed under a silversmith where his obvious talents could be much better employed. Even this proved no match for his talents and he was eventually moved to a *bijouterie* (jewellers) where he continued to be adept. Finally, continuing his interest in the jewellery trade he moved to Geneva, where he took on Swiss Citizenship and became known as Jacob Schweppe. He became very successful and wealthy as a *bijoutier* and was eventually admitted as a *maître-bijoutier*.

Having become successful and of adequate means, Schweppe was able to pursue his hobby as an amateur scientist. He studied the works of Joseph Priestley and, in particular, a paper of Priestley's entitled *Directions for Impregnating Water with Fixed Air* (1772). The

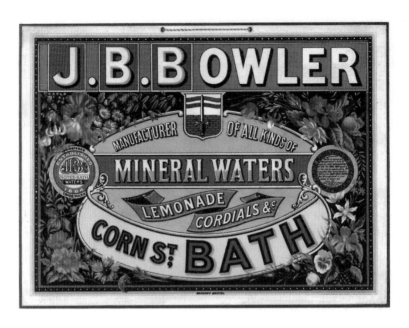

Above: Showcard of 1895 featuring J B Bowler Mineral Waters

Below: Bottles from the Bowler Collection.

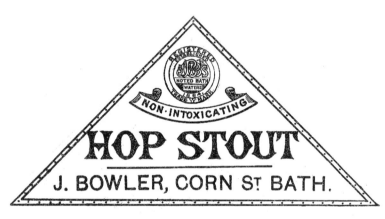

paper included the remark 'I do not doubt but that, by the help of a condensing engine, the water might be much more highly impregnated with the virtues of Pyrmont spring' (a naturally occurring mineral water). Interestingly Joseph Priestley lived at Calne and was a member of the Bath Philosophical Society.

Schweppe experimented with the production of carbonated water and by 1783 had produced an apparatus, known as the Geneva Apparatus or Geneva System, comprising a container for the generation of carbon dioxide from chalk and sulphuric acid, a gas holder, a pump and a carbonating vessel. This enabled him to go into commercial production. Eventually he opened a business in London and in 1803 expanded to three other towns including Bristol where his premises were in Philadelphia Street. The apparatus was widely adopted and that or similar systems were in use for many years.

What is also interesting in terms of a study of a Bath business is that Schweppe retired in 1799 and sold his business. Various partnerships were involved in the business until, in 1834, it was bought by two Bath businessmen – John Kemp-Welch, a wine merchant, and William Evill. Bowler's mineral water manufactory, as did those of his competitors, used very similar techniques and at this time the consumption of aerated water, either as soda water or as a flavoured cordial, grew very rapidly with the encouragement of the medical profession which believed it to be beneficial, and provided another good opportunity for those, such as Bowler, taking up the business.

Opposite: A selection of printed labels for Bowlers Mineral Waters Products.

Fig 14: The shop replica. (Photo BIHC)

The Artefacts in the Collection

The artefacts have been laid out in sections in the museum to give a representation of the Corn Street premises, the sections comprise:

1 The shop, a heavy machine shop, an office
2 The pattern shop, the brass foundry
3 The brass finishing/tinsmithing room
4 The mineral water factory

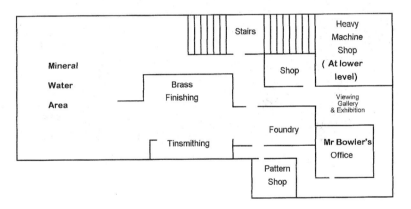

Fig. 13: *The arrangement of the Collection on the first floor of the Museum*

The Shop
The shop was not set up until 1912, after Jonathan Bowler's death, when the children, who were then running the business, apparently decided that people having to enter the workshops to place orders was not a good idea, possibly opening them to dangerous situations.

The original mahogany counter, now in the museum, was apparently bought from a defunct drapery business for some 15 shillings and their brass yard rule is still attached. Its provision in the drapers was previously arranged by Bowlers at much greater cost. The counter bears the scars of many years of the passage of metal across its surface and perhaps metal was occasionally cut on it. On the counter sit the scales, ex-butchers' shop, on which the metal being sold was weighed. Many items are located behind the counter and some hanging from the ceiling; the earliest of these must be the former pathological syringe of around 1800 that Bowler modified to sell as a grease gun. Other uses for this item had also been found in the past – Watt used one in his early steam engine experiments having seen it as a piston and cylinder.[1] There are gas jets which vary from the first type Bowler fitted, to a replacement type and then the later gas mantle fittings. None of the earlier fittings seem to have been disposed of or melted down, they were just put aside in their boxes. They may have been kept as spares for anyone still using the superseded fittings. There are sets of lock picks and many keys, and it is said that if one spare key was required then an extra one was cut and retained by Bowler against a further future possible requirement, but as the spares are not labelled (though they may have been in the past) it is difficult to assess how they could have been handed over to the right customer.

Bell hanging fittings are also to be seen in abundance and a typical servants call bell – perhaps to summon a servant to the drawing room – has been set up to demonstrate their operation. Many plumbing fittings are also to be seen from early water closets to wash basins and brass bath plugs. From the period when the company started working in the motor trade there are spares such as headlamps and speedometers. In 1919 Charlie Bowler bought at auction a Lot of 400 electric lamps, which he anticipated selling in the shop. Most of these are still there and wrapped having turned out to be, a) the wrong voltage and b) coloured dark blue. They were lamps in use by the Admiralty, in the First World War, to give 'night sight' on ships; later it was discovered that red lamps were better.

The rest of the items range from travelling irons to sugar loaf cutters, sheep shears, stands to hold gentlemen's pocket watches upright, and a tong device for holding up the hem of a ladies dress to avoid soiling on unmade and muddy roads.

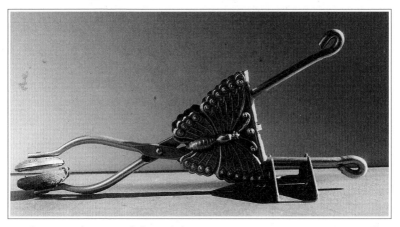

Fig 15: The Hem lifter. (Photo Don Browning, LRPS, BIHC)

The Engineering Business

What the contents of the engineering workshops comprised in Jonathan Bowler's time can only be surmised. The items now in the collection are those which were recovered from the Corn Street premises in 1969. Some may well have been purchased in Bowler's time but, as practically everything the Bowlers – father, sons and grandson - bought was at second-hand most of the items are pre-1911 anyway. The only possible guide is the early inventory found in one of the books but this, unfortunately, is not dated, though it had to be post-1912, as the inventory includes the Corner Shop which was created after Jonathan Bowler's death.

The Heavy Machine Shop

The Heavy Machine shop is provided at ground floor level with a viewing gallery from the first floor, thus allowing the machines to be run without danger to visitors. It has two fairly large, screw cutting, centre lathes. One is by Croft, Butterfield and Wilkinson (1870s) which has a capacity of 75 inches between centres and a bed gap swing of 32 inches; the other has a capacity of 56 inches between centres and a bed gap swing of 24 inches. There is also a horizontal miller by Smith and Coventry (1870s), a shaper by Collier and Co. (1850s) and an interesting pillar drill (Smith, Beacock & Tannet, Leeds, 1896) which is capable of drilling holes up to 2.5 inches in diameter and has a swing of thirty inches. Among the other miscellaneous items are a machine saw, a portable forge, a pipe-threading machine and a drill grinding machine.

An electric motor provides power to drive the machines, via line shafting and leather belts, much as they would have been driven at Corn Street though by a steam engine in the early days and later by a gas engine. Line shafting was used extensively in early machine shops so that one power source – a prime mover – could be used to drive many machines; in multi-floored buildings the drive was often extended from floor to floor. The line shaft has a wide pulley fitted adjacent to each machine to be driven, a leather belt then connects this to a sub-shaft which has two narrow pulleys fitted adjacent to each other (and opposite the wide pulley), known as fast and loose or drive and idle pulleys, the loose or idle being free to rotate on its shaft. A handle with a forked end is used to slide the belt from one narrow pulley to the other and across the wide pulley, thus turning the machine on or off, also on the sub-shaft is a three dimension pulley fitted over a similar one on the machine, though that on the machine is fitted in the opposite direction. Power is taken to the machine via a leather belt on the three dimension pulley allowing

*Opposite, Fig 16: The Shaping Machine
(Del, Don Browning, BIHC)*

66

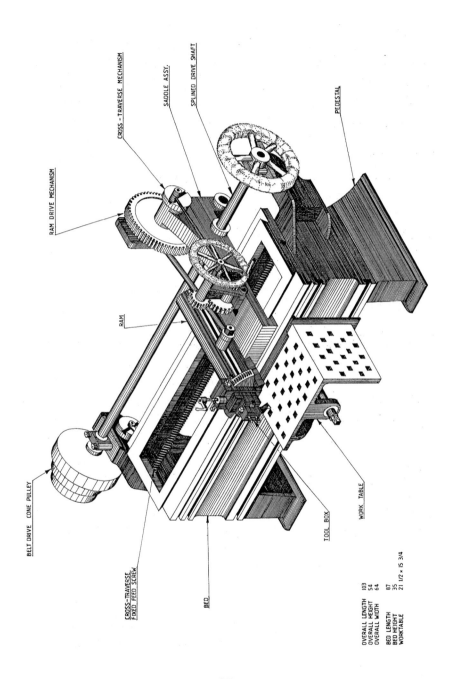

BELT DRIVE CONE PULLEY

RAM DRIVE MECHANISM

CROSS - TRAVERSE MECHANISM

SADDLE ASSY.

SPLINED DRIVE SHAFT

PEDESTAL

RAM

CROSS-TRAVERSE
FIXED FEED SCREW

BED

TOOL BOX

WORK TABLE

OVERALL LENGTH   103
OVERALL HEIGHT   54
OVERALL WIDTH   64

BED LENGTH   87
BED HEIGHT   35
WORKTABLE   21 1/2 x 15 3/4

the speed of the machine to be controlled depending on which diameter of the pulley is used. Whilst this form of drive was very efficient in using only one prime mover to drive a whole machine shop, or indeed a whole factory, it had many problems from the safety point of view, for example a loose item of clothing or long hair caught in a belt could drag an operator into a machine causing, in many cases, severe injury. As a result the system was eventually outlawed and individual enclosed machine drives by electric motors became the normal source of machine power.

For demonstration purposes the machine drives in the museum have been set up to start in turn, by time delay, to avoid excessive starting load on the motor.

There is also a turret lathe in the collection, though not on display, which is on permanent loan to the Radstock Railway Society. The turret lathe was perhaps one of the first moves towards automation in the machine tool industry as several tools could be set up in the turret and, when one operation had been completed, the turret was rotated and the next operation commenced. It also meant that a skilled setter could arrange the sequential operation and a semi-skilled operator could work the machine.

The Gallery

The gallery has an interesting display of photographs, some of Bowler's premises and family and some of Bath. Jonathan Bowler's Certificate of Indenture to Nathaniel Wilcox is also shown. There is a Griffin steam engine which once operated part of the machinery, a winch and a piece of line shafting to demonstrate the method of allowing machines to be driven or left to idle by, using a forked lever, sliding the leather belt one way or the other and also how their speed was changed by the use of a pulley having three different diameters.

The Office

The office has been set up to resemble the Corn Street office as closely as possible and has the original 'partners desk' where Bowler sat on one side and one of his daughters on the other. Bowler handled the orders and quotes and his daughter did the accounts and made copies of any correspondence sent out so that a reference back was available. On the desk is a slate which was used to record the smaller orders. The office includes much period bric a brac and interestingly four items made by Bowler's youngest son, James Edward. The items are a brass clock, a cotton reel tree and two figurines. On a visit to the museum in 1986 James' son (J B B's grandson), stated that his father, who specialised in ornate and delicate brasswork, had made these items.[2]

There is also a gas mantle light and a gas jet for melting sealing wax or perhaps pipe lighting, both in working order and lit during opening hours. A display cabinet shows a large collection of various glass shades for gas lights.

The Pattern Shop

This comprises many examples of the pattern makers' art from bevel gears to a pattern for the step of a circular staircase. The patterns were cut in wood, mainly well seasoned yellow pine, though for items which were likely to be reproduced many times a hard wood was sometimes used. On completion they were varnished, usually with shellac, to prevent the ingress of moisture and subsequent distortion during the next process of moulding.

Pattern making is one of the most skilled jobs in the metal working industry as if the pattern is not one hundred per cent accurate then any subsequent work is wasted. The pattern maker starts from an engineering drawing and has to interpret the information on that so that the correct solid shape is formed. Particular attention must be paid to the size of the pattern because it is going to be used to form a mould for the item to be cast in metal. The expansion of metal, when heated, requires that the pattern must be made large enough to account for this expansion so that when the metal cools the finished product is the correct size. To achieve this the pattern maker uses a 'contraction rule' which is usually double sided and has four sets of markings – an example in the pattern shop has a standard marking graduated up to 24 inches and then three other markings of 24 inches but all longer than the standard, thus allowing for different rates of expansion depending on which metal is to be cast. Table 9 shows the different rates of contraction for four metals.

Metal	Contraction per Foot
Cast Iron	0.10 inch
Brass	0.20 inch
Steel	0.25 inch
Aluminium	0.28 inch

Table 9*: The contraction of metal from molten to cold.*[3]

There is also a lathe in the pattern shop which was originally a metal lathe but has been modified by adding an additional headstock to make it wood turning. This seems to be in general keeping with the Bowler philosophy – why spend money on a special item when you have something which will do.

Other items are a dowel making machine, a small pillar drill and lots of early carpenters' hand tools.

The Foundry

Once a pattern has been produced it is taken to the foundry for casting. The casting is done by using moulding boxes and moulding sand. The moulding sand is ordinary sand which has been heated to a high temperature to burn off any impurities, thus taking on a reddish colouring. It is mixed with, typically, Fullers Earth, (a type of clay) to give it a degree of firmness so that, unlike a sand castle, it will not collapse when touched. The mixture is then damped with water and put into a bottom moulding box (called a drag). The pattern is then pressed into the sand to form a bottom half. Next a layer of fine dry sand (to allow the boxes to be parted) is spread across the top of the moulding box and another box placed over the top (this one called a cope). Moulding sand is added to this box and tamped down to form a good impression of the top of the pattern. Two holes are then made: a pouring gate to allow the molten metal to be poured in and a feeding gate which will allow air and gases to escape and also show when the mould is full as metal appears in it. The boxes are then separated, the pattern removed, and any imperfections made good with smoothing tools. Next the impression is dusted with a fine layer of plumbago dust (carbon), so that the surface to be formed is as smooth as possible, and then the two moulding boxes are put together again with a layer of dry separating sand between them; this avoids the two sections of moulding sand uniting and preventing easy separation of the boxes. The molten metal can then be poured through the pouring gate until the mould is full; when cool the moulding boxes are separated and the casting removed. Casting is usually done late in the day and the mould allowed to cool overnight. It is then taken to the finishing shop for final cleaning up and removal of surplus metal left at the pouring and feeding gates.

The furnace, which has not been set up to operate, has been recreated as found in the factory. What is not clear from examination of the documents in the Collection is whether Bowler did any casting of cast iron. The mounting brackets of his mineral water pump have his name cast into them but may have been cast elsewhere, possibly at the Walcot Foundry. The only references to be found in the documents are to gunmetal, brass or just castings. It is not impossible that he could have cast iron for, unlike the melting point of steel, which is quite high, some types of cast iron melt at 1071⁰C, or only 172⁰C higher than brass.

METAL	MELTING POINT Deg.C
Brass	899
Cast Iron	1071
Steel	1632

Table 10: *The melting points of various metals.*[4]

71

The Brass Finishing Room

The Brass Finishing room has a fine collection of six treadle lathes which must almost give a representative history of that type of lathe. Whether any of these machines are those originally bought by Jonathan Bowler is not known – he only had one 'foot' lathe in 1888 as revealed by a contemporary insurance policy, but certainly the oldest one 'has wooden standards and a wood bed surfaced with a steel bearing plate', though it has more recent additions.[5] The newest looks very similar to a Maudslay but has no markings of any description to indicate its maker. It is mounted on wooden standards and has a double treadle. A Maudslay treadle lathe with which it was compared is exhibited in the 'Synopsis' Collection at the National Museum of Science and Industry.

Bowlers would hire out any hand tools or other items which would show a profit and anything else which they had acquired in their auction purchases or scrap buying activities and found to be in good order or repairable. A good example of this is a clothes mangle which, according to the books, had been rented out to James Colmer though why Colmers, a large department store, should have needed a mangle is not known as they sold new clothes and haberdashery, etc.

There is also a Pagoda stove which would have been used in a large house or laundry which would keep several flat irons heated and ready for use so that as the one in use cooled another was immediately available. This item was probably very popular with employees in the winter but would have produced a stifling heat in summer. Other items reveal the connection with Bath's public house and hotel trade – there is a beer engine set and various barrel taps.

Among the most interesting items are the original illuminated sign which Bowler made for Davis & Son and some of the letters which were used to illuminate the Guild Hall for the Diamond Jubilee of Queen Victoria in 1897 and the Coronation of Edward VII in 1902.

Fig. 17: The oldest Treadle Lathe in the Collection (Del. Don Browning)

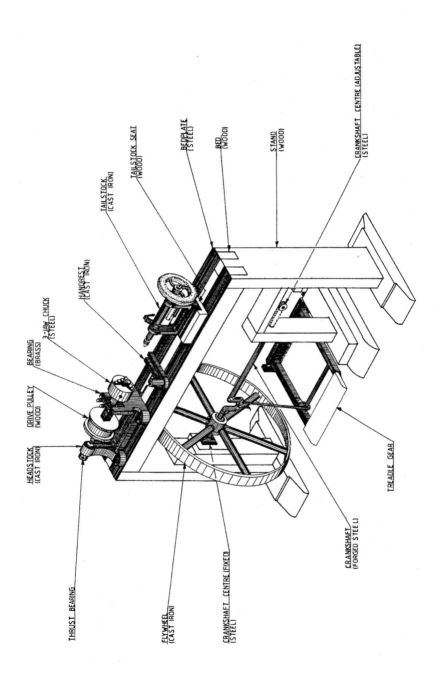

TAILSTOCK SEAT
(WOOD)

BEDPLATE
(STEEL)

BED
(WOOD)

STAND
(WOOD)

CRANKSHAFT CENTRE (ADJUSTABLE)
(STEEL)

TAILSTOCK
(CAST IRON)

HANDREST
(CAST IRON)

3-JAW CHUCK
(STEEL)

BEARING
(BRASS)

DRIVE PULLEY
(WOOD)

HEADSTOCK
(CAST IRON)

THRUST BEARING

FLYWHEEL
(CAST IRON)

CRANKSHAFT CENTRE (FIXED)
(STEEL)

CRANKSHAFT
(FORGED STEEL)

TREADLE GEAR

73

The Tinsmithing Shop

This has a collection of tinsmithing tools ranging from a very large pair of tin snips to a bending machine for sheet metal, and many hand tools. Adjacent is a wall-mounted, gas-heated lacquering oven, with typical laquered items displayed. Mounted on the wall adjacent to the oven is a fine collection of split dies which were used for cutting threads by hand.

The Mineral Water Manufactory

The mineral water manufactory has been set up to show the whole process of manufacture from the generation of carbon dioxide gas to the bottling plant. The main items are described and the mineral water manufacturing process is explained.

The Gas Generator

The gas generator comprises an oak tub mounted sideways with plated access holes top and bottom. Pipe accesses provide a water supply, a sulphuric acid input, and an exit pipe for the generated gas to be carried to the gas holder. The centres of the two ends of the barrel have a shaft passing through them and, fixed on the shaft inside the barrel, are paddles. The shaft is fitted with a pulley at one end to allow it to be rotated.

To generate the gas, crushed marble (calcium carbonate) was added through the top access plate; sulphuric acid and water were then added to make a diluted solution. Reaction would have started to produce gas immediately, but the paddle was rotated to agitate the mixture and speed up production. The speed of the paddles was adjusted to regulate the amount of gas produced to that required by the bottling machinery. The gas produced was led up to a gas holder through a lead pipe.

CARBON DIOXIDE GENERATION

$$CaCO_3 + H_2SO_4 = CO_2 + CaSO_4 + H_2O$$

Calcium Carbonate + Sulphuric Acid=Carbon Dioxide + Calcium Sulphate + Water

Crushed Marble   Gypsum

Plaster of Paris

NOTE: When Calcium Sulphate is heated to remove 75% of its moisture, Plaster of Paris is formed.

Fig. 18: The chemical reaction used to produce Carbon Dioxide Gas

Was this an opportunity missed by Bowler in not attempting to produce and sell Plaster of Paris? Perhaps he tried and found it not viable or not worthwhile.

The Gas Holder

The Gas Holder is made up of an oak barrel standing upright and without a top. Inside the barrel an inverted copper tub is placed, its diameter slightly smaller than that of the top of the inside of the barrel, the tub is counter weighted by a weight slightly less than its own so that a slightly pressured output will be available to feed gas to the aerating pump. A gas seal is made by filling the barrel with water to a level just above the bottom of the copper tub, when in its fully risen state. Gas was brought into the holder by means of a lead pipe which extended from the bottom to a point above the level of the water; it was led out of the gas holder by means of a pipe of similar length.

*Left, **Fig 19**: The Gas Generator; Right, **Fig 20**: The Gas Holder*

The Essence Room

Syrups were made here by mixing sugar, saccharin and flavouring or essences with tartaric acid added. The essences were mostly commercial products bought in from J W Bush. Herb products were ground and mixed on site for items such as Horehound beer. The syrup mixture was known as 'Twaddle' and a typical mix would have been one hundredweight of sugar, four pounds of tartaric acid, and four ounces of saccharin all mixed with fifty gallons of water and finally the appropriate flavouring. The prepared mixture was used to fill the syrup vessels located above the bottling machine. Adjacent to the essence room are the vats in which beer and ginger beer were made.

The Carpentry Section

Crates to contain the bottles for delivery were made within the factory. They would normally be made and repaired by the delivery men during the winter season when sales were not so great as in the warmer summer weather. There is a circular saw and a band saw in this section together with other tools required for the manufacture and repair work.

Fig 21: The Essence Room (Photo BIHC)

The Bottle Washing Machines

There are three machines that were used in the bottle washing process. The first machine involved putting the bottles into a pigeon-holed drum, the centre of which has a shaft through it, the two ends of the shaft sit in bearings on the sides of a trough of water. The lower half of the drum was therefore immersed in water. When the drum was rotated, the bottles were soaked and any sediment softened and the glue on the labels was also dissolved, allowing the labels to float off. Next the bottles were put on an internal washing machine and finished on another machine with a rotating brush if any deposits remained in the bottle.

The Bottling Area

The bottling area has one of Jonathan Bowler's original pumps, made by him in about 1870 – the cast iron stands bear his name. The pump is still in working order and is used to fill bottles for demonstration purposes, though carbon dioxide is not added. Connected to the pump via pipe work would have been a carbonating gas supply

Fig 22: The Carbonating Pump

and a gravity-fed water supply from a high level tank. The pump compressed the gas into the water and the resulting product of aerated water was stored in a reservoir cylinder. A turnover bottling machine (so called because, having placed the bottle in the machine, a handle is used to turn it over as part of the filling process) is connected to this reservoir and also to a high level syrup tub which would gravity feed the syrup. When a bottle is placed in the filling machine and turned over, a valve is opened and aerated water flows into the bottle, also a measured shot of syrup which is delivered via a cam and valve arrangement.

With the demonstration set up the bottle is merely filled with water. If the bottle being filled was of the Codd's type then the gas in the water would have forced a marble against a rubber seal in the top of the bottle to form a gas tight seal.

There is also a soda syphon filling machine which, whilst not connected, is able to be used to demonstrate the filling process. This machine has quite a heavy cast brass guard fitted as the pressure used for filling was up to 100 lbs. per square inch and a faulty bottle could be rather like an exploding grenade – in fact, one of Bowler's daughters (Louie) lost an eye due to an exploding bottle.

There are also corking machines, a labelling machine, a machine for inserting screw tops and two crown corking machines, one with an automatic hopper feed.

Many types of bottle are on display, including the interesting Hammond or egg bottle which is designed so that it can't be stood up thereby ensuring that the cork does not dry out and that the gas is kept in.

The Mineral Water Office

In the mineral water office can be found a set of pigeon-hole type drawers which were used to contain the bottle labels; many are still full. The normal business practice continued here, when one type of label was no longer required it was kept; labels still exist even from the days of Walter Annely. There are many hand tools associated with bottle filling and some old photographs, one of which is of the outside of the factory and includes a horse-drawn delivery cart.

Also on display here is Bowler's soda water dispenser which he hired out to public houses and hotels. A soda syphon was secured inside a cabinet slightly larger than itself. On top of the cabinet is a lever which can be operated by the insertion of a one penny (1d.) coin. When the lever is pressed it in turn presses the lever of the soda syphon thereby delivering a shot of soda water into the customer's whisky. The soda water was an optional extra.

The Almanac Collection

To assist in telling the world about his mineral water factory wares, other than his normal trade adverts, Bowler issued an almanac or calendar for each year from 1889 to his death in 1911. These were printed in full colour and featured prints of well known paintings such as 'The Horse Fair' on that of 1894. They were designed so that if required for later use as a print the border could be trimmed off and the remaining picture framed for use as a wall decoration. The quality of the prints is demonstrated by the fact that some of them have been hanging in the Camden Works Museum in close proximity to a window for many years and little or no fading is apparent. On the Almanacs the business is stated to have been established in 1864 which, presumably, is when Walter Annely began his mineral water manufacturing activities rather than the generally accepted date of 1872 for Bowler's official start.

These almanacs were sent out or given to good customers, but in common with the usual Bowler practice any spare ones were set aside. After Bowler's death the new company continued to produce them every year until the Great War intervened and by 1915 it was only possible to have a black and white print. No more were produced after that, the company relying on reputation and other advertising to bring it business.

Conclusion

This book has looked principally at the life of J B Bowler and the businesses he created or took over and ran. It has also positively demonstrated that industry, though small scale, existed in Bath from the late eighteenth century and was developing significantly in the nineteenth century.

The impression gained of J B Bowler is of an astute businessman with good entrepreneurial skills, tremendous energy in his early years and a good social conscience. There is no record of his education but, from reading his 'Book' it is obvious that he had a more than adequate grasp of both language and arithmetic. At the start of his 'Book', when he was 18 years-old, he describes himself as a scholar, presumably because he was still an apprentice. He started in business at a time when class differences were marked – some of his correspondence states quite tersely 'Come at once' or 'Please come immediately', 'Have ready by this afternoon, manservant will collect it'.

Bowler's businesses appear to have been successful, with the exception of the boot business which he quickly dropped, slowly increasing profitability and providing an excellent standard of living for his family, many of whom worked in the business. Most surprising is the fact that he left only some £10,000 – it seems more than likely that there was also undisclosed cash, though here it must be borne in mind that the family were taking a living from the business. Another strange thing arises from the visit of a Mr Marks to the Bowler Collection in 1987. He said that when he went to work for Stothert and Pitt in 1937, his first job was to go through the ledger and expenditure books looking for unpaid bills, he checked back to

1930 and discovered that 90% of unpaid bills were for small items supplied by Bowlers. An enquiry he made to Bowlers revealed that it was a longstanding agreement between J B Bowler and Sir Percy Stothert (1863-1929). It seems that at sometime around the turn of the century, Jonathan Bowler had been short of cash and had applied to Stothert for a loan. They reached a 'gentlemen's agreement' that in return for the loan, Stotherts would not be charged for items supplied by Bowlers. This had been in operation for around thirty years.[1]

After the children took over the business no great effort seems to have been made at innovation apart from the venture into motor repairs. The business was allowed to tick over relying on reputation and ability. Though it has to be said that they did keep abreast of new developments and were excellent service providers for practically any trade requiring engineering materials, including the public utilities. Their major flaw in the latter years was the time taken to provide service in the shop; the author of this study recalls waits of two hours or more being not unusual. This has been confirmed by several visitors to the collection, one of whom said that a visit to Bowlers or Membreys (another Bath engineering supplier) was a favourite outing for apprentices in Bath. Ernest had taken over the business but few of the rest of the family were interested in working there.

With many businesses the spark, enthusiasm and innovation of the founder is not followed through by his successors and it is quite common for the business to demise in the third generation.

What the true financial state of the business through the years was is now impossible to assess. The figures quoted are the best available though they certainly would not stand up to an accountant's scrutiny. An enquiry to Companies House revealed that all the official returns had been destroyed in 1995.[2] Whether all the cash that came into the business found its way into the books is not certain: could the sharp rise in turnover in 1911 be because Charlie was not then familiar with 'managing' the books? It is interesting to note when looking at the weekly entries in some of the engineering Income Expenditure Books that whilst the income entries do not always fill one page they never go over into a second; when the page is full the entries cease. Did they close the shop for the rest of the week when the page was full? There are also some books which seem to overlap for no apparent reason. Then there is the statement by Mrs Agnes Joyce that William Woodman Bowler always carried, and could not be separated from, a Gladstone Bag, and that he had told his daughter, when she found him counting the contents one day, that it contained thousands of pounds.[3]

There is still scope for further study of the 80,000 or so documents, of 'Bowler's Book', the other books of the business and family details. Some of the early correspondence relates to Jonathan's brother who had set up a nursery business in Crosby, Isle of Man, and whom Bowler seemed to be supplying with materials for heating and glass for his greenhouses. Many of the items sent via the railway company arrived broken and led to protracted correspondence for compensation. Jonathan's interest in social welfare, many years before the introduction of the National Health Service and the State, led to his association with the Royal and Ancient Order of Buffaloes and the Order of Foresters of which he was treasurer for many years. There was also his gambling instinct which gave rise to his share investments – the books show dividends from the Fullers Earth Company though no others were discovered in this study.[4]

This study of Jonathan Burdett Bowler's business has demonstrated:

1. Bowler's wide range of business interests with diversification into mineral water manufacturing, property and boots etc.
2. The importance of the mineral water business as the money spinner due to Bowler's astuteness in acquiring Walter Annely's business at a time when, with medical support, it was becoming fashionable to drink this product.
3. His frugal approach (never buy new if you can get second-hand)

kept costs low but could have had shortcomings in the long run. He was a very 'make do and mend' man, a characteristic which seemed to follow through the family to the closure of the business.

4. The importance of industrial conservation as a means of understanding the past. The Bowler Collection Museum is not only a setting for the interested visitor but is used educationally by schools for lessons in Victorian industrial history.

5. The importance of Bath industry and in particular the number of metal trades businesses mostly concentrated in the riverside district.

6. The north-south divide symbolised by the social barrier at the bottom of Milsom Street which reflected the upper-class north and the concentration of trades and their workshops in the south.

7. The fact that Bath's history is still much misunderstood is underpinned – the myth of genteel Bath is perpetuated for commercial reasons because it is much easier to sell Jane Austen's Bath than industrial Bath.

8. It was possible, even in Victorian times, for an able person from humble beginnings to rise in social status and become a respected businessman.

REFERENCES, NOTES AND BIBLIOGRAPHY

Primary Sources
The Bowler Collection Archive – around 80,000 bills, invoices and letters, some 200 books of the business and miscellaneous ephemera.
The Bath Street Directories 1783-1866.
The Bath Rate Book.
The *Bath Herald*
Census of population Records.
St Katherine's House Records of Births, Deaths and Marriages.
J.B. Bowler's Tombstone, Small Combe Cemetery.

References and Notes
INTRODUCTION
1. Interview with Russell Frears, Corn Street to Camden Works, 9997, Tape No. 150, BIHC.
2. The Bowler Collection Archive. Unpublished typescript, Stella Pierce7 Bath Industrial Heritage Centre, 1984.
3. *Ibid.*
4. K.S. Inglis, *Journal of Ecclesiastical History*, vol. 11 no. 1 (London 1960), Patterns of Religious Worship in 1851, (W. S. F. Pickering, The 1851 Religious Census-a useless experiment?, *The Journal ofthe British Sociological Association*, 1967, p.403, ref 33).

CHAPTER 1
1. Bowler's Book, Bowler Archive (BIHC)
2. *Ibid.*
3. Rate Book, 1851, Bath City Archive
4. Bowler's Book, BIHC
5. *Ibid*
6. Post Office Directory, Bath, 1856
7. Bowler's Book, BIHC
8 Bowler's Cash/Day Book, 1872-1875,(pl), BIHC.

CHAPTER 2
1. A Bowler Chronology, unpublished typescript (BIHC), GAC, November, 1995, (p5)
2. *Ibid*
3. *Ibid*, (p6)
4. *Hutchinson Multimedia Encyclopedia*, Oxford, 1996

5. *Bath Herald*, Bath, Monday, April 11, 1881, (P3)
6. JBB's Noted Bath Waters, unpublished typescript, C. Liebenrood, BIHC, 1993, p.2.
7. Document in Miscellaneous Bowler Information, Curators Office, BIHC. Companies House documentation. Bristol Commercial Library.
8. Family Tree and Miscellaneous Bowler Inforrnation Curators Office, BIHC.
9. Interview with Ernest Bowler by Russell Frears and Kenneth Hudson, Tape No. 36, BIHC.

CHAPTER 3
1. Memorandum of Association, Miscellaneous Bowler Information Curators Office, BIHC.
2. Interview with Ernest Bowler by Russell Frears and Kenneth Hudson, Tape No. 36, BIHC.
3. A study of the Companies activities during The Great War, unpublished typescript, G. A. Christie, BIHC, January, 1995 (pl)
4. *Ibid*, p.3.
5. *Ibid*, p.4.
6. *Ibid*, p.4.
7. *Ibid*, p.9.
8. Rate Book, 1917-1920, Bath City Archive.

CHAPTER 4
1. Bath Street Directories, 1783, Bailey; 1784, Bailey; 1787, Bristol & Bath; 1791, Bailey; 1800, Robbins; 1805, Browne, 1809, Browne; 1812, Wood & Cunningham; 1819, Gye; 1822, Gye; 1824, Keene; 1826, Keene; 1829, Keene; 1831, 1833, Keene; 1837, Silverthorne; 1841, Sliverthorne; 1846, Silverthorne; 1850, Clarke; 1856, Robinson; 186061, the Post Office; 1866, the Post Office. In the Bath Reference Library
2. *Victorian Engineering*, Rolt, L.T.C., London, 1970, pp 76-77.
3. Interview with Ernest Bowler by Russell Frears and Kenneth Hudson, Tape No. 36, BIHC.
4. The Early Years of Stothert & Pitt, Torrens, H., J*ournal of the Bristol Industrial Archaeological Society*, Vol. 9, 1976, pp 24-31.
5. *Industrial Archaeology in Britain*, R.A. Buchanan. London, 1972. (p 103)
6. *Bath at Work*, Duncan Harper, Bath 1989, p.46.
7. *Ibid*, p.68.
8. *Schweppes, The First 200 Years*, Douglas A Simmons, London, 1983, pp 11-21.

CHAPTER 5
1. Exhibit in the National Museum of Science and Industry (Power).
2. Typescript in miscellaneous Bowler information, Curators Office.
3. *Workshop Technology, Part One, An Introductory Course*, W.A.J. Chapman,

4th Ed., London, 1962, p.67.
4. *Fowler's Mechanics' and Machinists' Pocket Book*, 1917, Scientific Publishing, Manchester, p.98.
5. *Treadle Lathes at Bath Industrial Heritage Centre*, Don Browning, BIHC, 1997 pp 13 & 17.

CONCLUSION
1. Typescript in Miscellaneous Bowler Information, Curator's office, BIHC.
2. Companies House, Bowlers registered as Company No. 120, 624
3. Interview with Mrs May Bowler on lO/02/95. Tape No 134, BIHC.
4. Interview with Ernest Bowler by Russell Frears and Kenneth Hudson,1972, Tape No. 36, BIHC.

NOTE
Where invoices, and correspondence, etc are quoted, unless otherwise noted, they are to be found filed with the Bowler Miscellaneous Papers in the BIHC Archive under the appropriate year and indexed alphabetically, thus avoiding excessive referencing.

Bibliography
A History of Machine Tools, Ian Bradley, MAP Technical Publications, 1972.
Bath, A Social History 1680-1850 or A Valley of Pleasure yet a Sink of Iniquity, R.S. Neale, London, 1981.
Bath, Some Encounters with Science, W. J. Williams and D. M. Stoddart, Bath 1978.
Bath at Work, Duncan Harper, Bath 1989.
Bath, A New History, Graham Davis and Penny Bonsall, Keele University Press, 1996.
Bath History, Vol VI, ed. B.J. Buchanan, Bath 1996.
Bristol Brass: A History of the Industry, J. Day, 1973.
Fowler's Mechanics' and Machinists' Pocket Book 1917, Scientific Publishing Co., (Manchester).
Industrial Archaeology of the Bristol Region, Angus Buchanan and Neil Cossins, Newton Abbot, 1969.
Industrial Archaeology in Britain, R.A. Buchanan, London, 1972.
Local History in England, W. G. Hoskins, 3rd. edition, 5th. imp., New York 1993.
Mainly Codd's Wallop, Roy Morgan, Wellingborough, 1974.
Portrait of Bath, John Haddon, London, 1989.
Soft Drinks, Colin Emmins, Haverfordwest, 1991.
The Bath Gas Light and Coke Company, some notes on the history of the Company 1818-1819, Ellery, C. Stafford, Bath, 1918.
The Bowler Collection, Kenneth Hudson and Russell Frears, BIHC, 1978.
The Cabinet Making Trade of Bath, 1740-1964, Keevil, H. F., Bath, 1964.

The Cloth Industry in the West of England, J. de L. Mann, Gloucester, 1971.
The Early Water Supply of Bath, Shickle, C. W., Bath,1917.
The Evolution of Glass Bottles for Carbonated Drinks, Olive Talbot, (Reprint from *Post Medieval Archaeology,* Vol. 8, 1974).
The Industrial Archaeology of Bath, R.A. Buchanan, Bath, 1969.
The Mechanical Side of Mineral Water Manufacture, Pyramid, The Mineral Water Trade Review, London, 1934.
Workshop Technology, Part One, An Introductory Course, W.A.J. Chapman, 4th Ed., London, 1962.
Workshop Technology, Part Two, W.A.J. Chapman, 3rd Ed., London, 1963.

Journals
Journal of Ecclesiastical History, vol. 11 no. 1 (London 1960), K.S. Inglis, Patterns of Religious Worship in 1851, (W. S. F. Pickering, The 1851 Religious Census- a useless experiment?, *The Journal ofthe British Sociological Association,* 1967, p.403, ref 33).
Journal of the Bristol Industrial Archaeological Society, Vol. 9, 1976

Unpublished Typescripts at the Bath Industrial Heritage Centre
Transcript of Bowlers' workshops inventory, G.A. Christie, BIHC, 1995.
Typescript, Jonathan Bowler, Victorian Entrepreneur, G. A. Christie, BIHC, undated.
A Bowler Chronology, G. A. Christie, BIHC, 1995.
Notes on extracts from Bath Directories, BIHC.
JBB's Noted Bath Waters, C. Liebnrood, BIHC, 1963.
The Almanac Collection, List of Titles and Quantities, BIHC, (undated)
J.B. Bowler and Sons, A Study of the Company's Activities during the Great War, G.A. Christie, BIHC, 1995.
The Bowler Collection Archive, Stella Pierce, BIHC, 1984.
Visit from Edward George Burdett Bowler, 30th Oct. 1986, and from Ivy Doris Bowler (née Beaverstock) notes by Alan Hack, 1987.
Information revealed by recent Archive Cataloguing, Alan Hack, undated.
Notes on visit from Mr Marks (ex Stothert & Pitt employee), Alan Hack, 1987.
Treadle Lathes at Bath Industrial Heritage Centre, Don Browning, BIHC, 1997.

Audio Tape Cassettes
Interview with Russell Frears Corn Street to Camden Works. 9997, Tape No. 150, BIHC.
Interview with Mrs Mav Bowler. daughter of Ernest Bowler and Great-Grand-Daughter of J.B Bowler. 1995, Tape No 134, BIHC.
Interview with Mrs Agnes Joyce, Undated, Tape No 63, BIHC.
Interview with Ernest Bowler by Russell Frears and Kenneth Hudson,1972,

Tape No. 36, BIHC

Multimedia
Hutchinson Multimedia Encyclopedia, Oxford, 1996

NB
Where drawings or photographs are not otherwise credited they are by the author.

INDEX

About the Author

Ken Andrews was born in Bristol in 1934 and has always lived there apart from two years National Service with the Royal Corps of Signals.

After leaving Cotham Grammar School he was apprenticed to the Post Office Engineering Department with whom he served for over forty years, the final years with the privatised British Telecom. He retired in 1991 as a Regional Works Manager for Trunk Services in the south-west of England.

He has always had an interest in local history and industrial archaeology. When a new master's course in local and regional history was advertised by Bath Spa University College he enrolled and, in due course, was awarded an MA Degree. The dissertation for his degree was on the Bowler Collection, located at the Bath Industrial Heritage Centre, and led to the production of this book.